Bridge to
IELTS

Pre-intermediate–Intermediate Band 3.5 to 4.5

Workbook

Louis Rogers

NATIONAL GEOGRAPHIC LEARNING | CENGAGE Learning®

Australia • Brazil • Japan • Korea • Mexico • Singapore • Spain • United Kingdom • United States

Bridge to IELTS Workbook

Louis Rogers

Publisher: Jason Mann

Senior Commissioning Editor: John Waterman

Editorial Project Manager: Karen White

Development Editor: Rhona Snelling

Head of Marketing and Communications:
  Michelle Cresswell

Project Editor: Tom Relf

Production Controller: Elaine Willis

Art Director: Natasa Arsenidou

Cover design: Vasiliki Christoforidou

Text design: Maria Papageorgiou

Compositor: Maria Papageorgiou

Audio: Produced by James Richardson at
  The Soundhouse Studios

ISBN: 978-1-133-31896-5

National Geographic Learning
Cheriton House, North Way, Andover, Hampshire, SP10 5BE
United Kingdom

Cengage Learning is a leading provider of customised learning solutions with office locations around the globe, including Singapore, the United Kingdom, Australia, Mexico, Brazil and Japan. Locate our local office at **international.cengage.com/region**

Cengage Learning products are represented in Canada by Nelson Education Ltd.

Visit National Geographic Learning online at **ngl.cengage.com**
Visit our corporate website at **www.cengage.com**

CREDITS

Although every effort has been made to contact copyright holders before publication, this has not always been possible. If contacted, the publisher will undertake to rectify and errors or omissions at the earliest opportunity.

Photos
The publisher would like to thank the following sources for permission to reproduce their copyright protected photographs:

Alamy pp4 (David R. Frazier Photolibrary, Inc.), 7 bl (CF Photos), 12 (Robert Tracey), 16 t (TravelStockCollection - Homer Sykes), 17 (Greg Balfour Evans), 18 t (Adrian Sherratt), 22 t (Keith Dannemiller), 27 (GoGo Images Corporation), 36 tl (Stefano Politi Markovina), 37 bl (CulturalEyes - AusGS2), 40 (John Warburton-Lee Photography), 42 c (Travel Pictures), 42 r (Jon Arnold Images Ltd), 43 (Thomas Imo), 44 l (Robert Daly), 45 r (Aardvark), 46 (vario images GmbH & Co.KG), 46 l (Bon Appetit), 53 bc (JoeFox), 53 bl (Barrie Harwood), 53 br (Kelly Shannon Kelly), 53 tr (Detail Nottingham), 54 cl (Paula Solloway), 54 cr (Ted Foxx), 59 br (Somos Images), 6o tl (John Warburton-Lee Photography), 61 br (Robert Harding World Imagery), 61 tl (imagebroker), 66 (PhotoAlto), 72 l (CuboImages srl), 82 tr (Wavebreak Media ltd), 83 t (David Noton Photography), 84 bc;86 r (Oleksiy Maksymenko), 87 t (Peter Phipp/ Travelshots.com), 89 c (Darkened Studio), 89 t (shinypix), 92 cr (LOOK Die Bildagentur der Fotografen GmbH), 92 tl (Photo Provider Network), 92 tr (sandy young), 96 t (Myrleen Pearson); Amanda Grobbecker p56 r. **Corbis UK Ltd** pp21 (Image Source), 88 r (Ralf-Finn Hestoft); Corbis UK Ltd. pp14 b (Imaginechina), 14 c (Zhou Chao/Epa), 38 (George Tiedemann/GT Images/Cor), 76 b;77 t (Keren Su), 78 b (Dlillc), 83 c (Roland Gerth), 87 c (Cameron Davidson), 92 bl (Laura Doss), 96 b (Tanya Constantine/Blend Images); Fotoe p85. **Getty Images** pp14 t; 36 bl (David Santiago Garcia), 37 tl (MICHEL GANGNE/AFP), 39 (Hulton Archive), 42 l (Jimmy LL Tsang), 44 r (Michael Blann), 49 (Travis Dove/The Boston Globe), 54 tl (moodboard), 58 (Image Source), 59 tl (Caroline Schiff), 59 tr (Comstock Images), 6o cc (Jane Sweeney), 6o tc (Muntasir Mamun/kewkradong.com), 61 tr (Sami Sarkis), 64 (Chris Tobin), 68 l (Rob Lewine), 72 r (photosindia), 73 c (Westend61), 73 t (Marvin Fox), 76 b (Kelly Cheng Travel Photography), 79 b (M.M. Sweet/Flickr), 80 b (pasmal/a.collectionRF), 81 (Dennis Macdonald), 84 ;88 l (Apic), 89 b (Sylvain Sonnet). **iStockphoto** pp6 t (YinYang), 7 b (Mark Rose), 7 br (stocknroll), 7 cl (James Brey), 7 cr (Jostaphot), 7 tl (PeskyMonkey), 7 tr (Karen Low Phillips), 13 c (Chris Hepburn), 13 tl (Liz Leyden), 20 l (franckreporter), 25 (Jacob Wackerhausen), 28 (franckreporter), 31 (Lisa-Blue), 45 l (Elena Elisseeva), 54 br (Joe Gough), 69 b (sorendls), 70 (Chris Bernard), 90 (Claudia Dewald); 92 br (Peter Zaharov), 92 cl (Reuben Schulz), 95 (1MoreCreative); JupiterImages p91 (Creatas); Kia Motors p86 l;King of the Court p52 l (Jake Wilson). **John Waterman** p68 r. **Maria Papageorgiou** pp23 bl;24 tl;38 t;50 br;50 c;57 ;75. **NASA** p84 tr. **Press Association Images** p87 b (Associated Press). **Rex Features** p94. **Shutterstock** pp6 b (Nowik), 9 l (Wild Arctic Pictures), 9 r (hxdbzxy), 10 (wavebreakmedia ltd), 13 bl (Stephen Finn), 13 r (godrick), 14 t (billybear), 15 (billybear), 16 b (Michael Rubin), 16 t (echo3005), 17 t (echo3005), 18 br (kroomjai), 18 l (Christian Delbert), 20 b (Nicemonkey), 22 b (Konstantin Chagin), 23 br (Allison Hays - Allicat Photography), 23 l (CREATISTA), 23 tr (Albert Campbell), 24 l (Andresr), 24 l (kroomjai), 24 r (Carlos E. Santa Maria), 26 b (kroomjai), 26 t (izarizhar), 29 (My Portfolio), 30 (Marcel Vint), 34 b (jelome), 34 t (Tupungato), 36 r (Luciano Mortula), 37 br (E.O.), 37 t (Zeca Arruda), 41 b (Image Focus), 41 c (Solid), 41 t (PedroVieira), 46 c (Kurhan), 48 (Dmitry Kalinovsky), 50 c (Palsur), 50 cl (SuperVector), 51 (Dmitriy Shironosov), 52 cr (gladcov), 52 r (Yellowj), 52 tl (iconspro), 53 tc (Ralf Gosch), 53 tl (meirion matthies), 54 bl (shock), 54 tr (Galina Barskaya), 56 l (Terry Chan), 59 bl (Amy Nichole Harris), 59 cc (o6photo), 60 b (EpicStockMedia), 6o cl (Platslee), 6o r (Rafal Cichawa), 61 bl (Ralph Loesche), 61 cr (Asaf Eliason), 62 b (Muriel Lasure), 62 l (Albert Campbell), 63 cl (mashe), 68 (Michal Modzelewski), 69 c (AISPIX by Image Source), 69 t (iofoto), 71 (Zurijeta), 72 tl (Hluboki Dzianis), 73 b (2399), 76 l (Christian Delbert), 78 t (FloridaStock), 78 tl (Nicemonkey), 80 t (Dudarev Mikhail), 82 b (Laborant), 82 tl (Olivier Le Moal), 83 b (kwest), 86 b (Pro-Studio), 95 (kwest), 95 (Michal Modzelewski), 99 (Aleksandar Mijatovic). **Shutterstock Footage** p6 cl. **Thinkstock** pp41 cr (Hemera), 50 t (Hemera), 61 cl (Hemera), 63 t (Hemera). **Zooid Pictures** p88 c.

Text
The publisher would like to thank the following sources for permission to reproduce their copyright protected texts:

Universities UK for the figure on page 33 "Percentage of full-time first degree students in each subject area, 1994/95 – 2008/09" from *Patterns of higher education institutions in the UK: 10th report*, September 2010, Chart 3, p.30, copyright © Universities UK; Republic of Cyprus Ministry of Education and Culture for the figure on page 33 "Cypriot and foreign students in Cyprus and Cypriot students studying abroad", www.highereducation.ac.cy, copyright © Ministry of Education and Culture; LV for the table on page 73 "The cost of raising a child tops £200,000", 24 February 2010, http://community.lv.com. Reproduced by permission of LV= Life and Pensions

Illustrations by: Kevin Jones Agency

Printed in China by RR Donnelley
1 2 3 4 5 6 7 8 9 10 – 16 15 14 13 12

Bridge to IELTS Contents

Home

LISTENING

1   Put the sentences in order to make a dialogue.

1   **Elena:** Anton, this is Luc. He's from France.
2   **Anton:** Nice to meet you, too! I'm from Russia.
3   **Luc:** I'm a new student, too!
4   **Luc:** Are you a new student?
5   **Elena:** Hello, Anton!
6   **Elena:** I'm fine, thanks. And you?
7   **Luc:** Hello, Anton. Nice to meet you.
8   **Anton:** Yes, I am.
9   **Anton:** I'm very well, thanks.
10 **Anton:** Hi, Elena! How are you?

2   🎧 1 Listen and check.

Living IELTS

INTRODUCING PEOPLE

1   Complete the dialogue. Use the words below.

> this is (x2)   to meet you   you, too

A: Rochila, ¹ _____ Suleiman. Suleiman,
² _____ Rochila. Rochila's a science
student, too.
B: Hi, Suleiman. Nice ³ _____ .
C: Hello, Rochila. Nice to meet ⁴ _____ .

2   🎧 2 Listen and check.

Grammar

Present simple of BE

1 Rewrite the sentences using the full form.

1 We're students.

_____

2 I'm from Germany.

_____

3 They're from Greece.

_____

4 She's French.

_____

5 London's in the UK.

_____

6 I'm her brother.

_____

2 Correct the mistakes in the sentences.

1 They isn't in the science department.
2 Rochila are from Nepal.
3 London are in the USA. It are the capital city of England.
4 I is not from the UAE.
5 Agnes aren't from China.
6 She be from Germany.

3 Match the questions with the short answers below.

1 Is she French?
2 Are you a new student?
3 Is he from Germany?
4 Are they on the tour?
5 Is your name Agnes?

a Yes, I am.
b No, she isn't.
c Yes, they are.
d Yes, he is.
e No, it isn't.

Pronunciation

Vowel sounds – /ɒ/ /ei/ /ai/

1 🔘3 Listen to the pronunciation of the words in bold.

/ɒ/	/ei/	/ai/
what	**name**	**I**
fly	eye	eight
late	not	hot
stop	hate	my

2 Read the words in the table. Are they in the correct column? Correct any mistakes.

3 🔘4 Listen and check.

4 🔘4 Listen again and repeat the words.

Vocabulary

Making friends

1 Complete the answers with the words in the box.

meet chat start go out say

1 Let's go and _____ hello to Tom.
2 I _____ people from my course every Friday in the café.
3 The easiest way to _____ a conversation in England is to talk about the weather.
4 I _____ with friends after lessons.
5 I like to _____ to someone new every day.

2 🔘5 Listen and check.

Living in halls

Living in halls is an exciting time for many students. It is often the first time living away from home.

The rooms are usually quite **small**. The windows are also small so it can be quite dark inside. For some students it is often too **hot**, because the heating is controlled by the university and not the individual student. The beds are comfortable, but it is not five-star luxury.

Living with lots of other students can also be very noisy.

So why are these **dark**, **uncomfortable** and **noisy** rooms popular? They could rent a house with friends or get a private bedsit or flat, but many students love halls. Why? You meet some of the best friends you make in your life. It is such an exciting time that students quickly forget the halls and just have fun meeting others from around the world!

READING

1 **'Halls of residence' (or 'Halls') are a type of accommodation for students in the UK. Read the text and answer the questions.**

1 Where do most students live before going to university?
2 Why are the rooms sometimes dark?
3 What can be the problem living with other students?
4 What other types of accommodation are there for students?
5 Why do students love halls?

2 **Write the opposites of the words below using words in bold from the text.**

1 big   _____
2 bright   _____
3 cold   _____
4 comfortable   _____
5 quiet   _____

VOCABULARY

ADJECTIVES TO DESCRIBE ROOMS

Complete the descriptions. Use the words below.

flat   untidy   house   cold   student hall   comfortable   bedsit

1   I live in a small _____ in Moscow.

4   I don't like my _____ because it is much smaller than my parent's house.

2   My family's _____ is big.

5   This chair is very _____. I could go to sleep in it.

3   I live in a _____, everything is in one room.

6   This room is _____. Can you put the heating on?

7   How do you study in that bedroom? It's so _____.

Listening

1 Label the pictures with the words in the box.

> bed   bookshelves   desk   lamp
> sofa   table   window   laptop

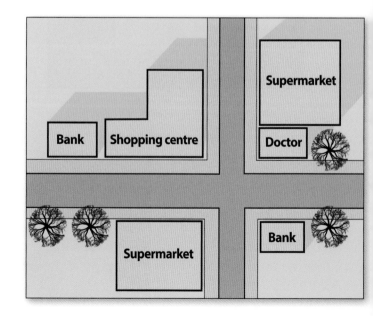

2  Listen to Vera talking on the phone. Choose the correct answers.

1 Vera is phoning her *sister / mother / uncle*.
2 Vera's mum is worried about *food / friends / lessons*.
3 Vera is living in *a flat / a house / student halls*.
4 Vera's room is picture *A / B*.

3 Listen again and complete the sentences.

1 There isn't an _____ or a _____ in my room.
2 There is a _____ in the living room.
3 There is a _____ next to my desk.
4 There aren't any _____ but there is a _____ for my laptop.
5 There is a _____ in the living room.

Grammar

THERE IS / THERE ARE

1 Complete the sentences with *is* or *are*.

1 There _____ a table in the kitchen.
2 There _____ two sofas in the living room.
3 There _____ a shop under the flat.
4 There _____ forty bedrooms in our student halls.

2 Choose the correct answers.

1 *Is there / Are there* a lot of people in your lessons?
2 *Is there / Are there* many shops here?
3 *Is there / Are there* a 24-hour computer room at the university?
4 *Is there / Are there* many people from Saudi Arabia here?
5 *Is there / Are there* a bank near here?

3 Write sentences to describe the town in the map. Use the words in the box with *there is/ isn't* or *there are/aren't*.

> shopping centre   restaurant   bank   café
> supermarket   post office   doctor's

WRITING

A PERSONAL DESCRIPTION

1 Read the description of the University of Svalbard and answer the questions below. Write full sentences.

University Centre Svalbard, Norway

Home | Education | Exams | Forum | Links | News & Events | Contact

The University Centre in Svalbard is in Norway. There are only four courses for students – biology, geology, geophysics and technology. There are 350 students in the university. There is a telephone in every bedroom. There is a library, but most books and information are electronic.

The university is in a place called Longyearbyen. There are 2000 people in Longyearbyen. There are lots of restaurants, but they are expensive. Norway is one of the most expensive countries in Europe.

1 How many courses are there at the university?

_____

2 How many students are there?

_____

3 Is there a library?

_____

4 Is there a telephone?

_____

5 Are there any restaurants?

_____

WRITING SKILLS

WORD ORDER

2 Correct the mistakes in the questions.

1 What your name is?
2 Where you are from?
3 What is home your near?
4 What your home is like?
5 How people many in your town live?
6 What do you in the evenings do?

3 Match the answers with the questions in activity 2.

a There is a supermarket and a restaurant near my home.
b My name is Paul.
c I go out to a restaurant with my friends.
d I live in a small flat. There is a bedroom and a kitchen.
e There are lots of people. Maybe 200 000.
f I am from Russia.

4 Answer the questions in activity 2 for you.

THE GOOD LANGUAGE LEARNER

1 Do you think you are a good language learner? Write down the things you do well as a language learner.

2 Look at the list below. Tick (✔) the sentences that are true for you. Put a cross (✗) next to the sentences that are not true for you.

1 I look at my work after class and study any new materials again. ☐
2 I have a vocabulary book to write new words in. ☐
3 I practise using the new vocabulary and don't just remember the meaning. ☐
4 I don't translate every word. I try to use a monolingual dictionary. ☐
5 I read English outside the classroom. ☐
6 I listen to English outside the classroom. ☐
7 I use English (not my own language) in class. ☐
8 I check my work for mistakes. ☐
9 I practise new grammar with a self-study book or online. ☐

3 Complete the table with four examples of your good language learner skills.

Things I do now	How I do them
I chat online in English.	I write messages on Facebook in English.

My goals

THE GOOD LANGUAGE LEARNER

1 Complete the table below with four goals for your future.

Things I do now	How I am going to do them
I don't practise new grammar	Buy a grammar book and practise any new grammar points.

2 Look at your goals again in two weeks and see what progress you make.

SPEAKING PART 1

In the first part of the speaking test you are asked questions about familiar topics, such as home, family, work, studies and interests. This part lasts four to five minutes.

1 Read these questions and think about your answers.

What do you like doing in your free time?
Why do you like doing these things?
How much time do you spend on these hobbies?
What would you do if you had more free time?

2 Practise speaking by answering the questions in activity 1.

3 7 Listen to two students answering the questions. Which student do you think is better?

LUCIA

KHALID

4 7 Listen again and tick who makes the mistakes (Lucia or Khalid).

		Lucia	Khalid
Question 1	The answer is very short.		
Question 2	The student speaks very quietly.		
Question 3	The student speaks very quickly.		
Question 4	The student forgets a word.		

5 Answer the questions in activity 1 again. Try to avoid the mistakes in activity 4.

Exam Tip

Complete the tips below using words from the box.

understand   clearly   *synonym   full

1 Try to give _____ answers, not just one or two words.
2 Try to speak _____ so it is easy for the examiner to hear you.
3 Don't speak too fast or it can be difficult to _____ you.
4 When you can't remember a word, try to think of a _____ or explain the word.

* **Synonym:** a word that has the same meaning as another word. For example: *My bedroom is very light / bright.*

Festivals

THE EDINBURGH FESTIVAL Fringe

A   The Edinburgh Festival Fringe is the largest arts **festival** in the world. It takes place every August for three weeks in Edinburgh, Scotland's capital city.

B   Every year thousands of **shows** take place and there is something for everyone. There are very **famous** performers in the world of entertainment and unknown artists just starting their careers. Shows include theatre, comedy, dance, music, exhibitions and events.

C   The festival started in 1947, when eight uninvited theatre groups arrived to **perform** at the Edinburgh International Festival. Not being part of the official programme of the International festival didn't stop these performers – they just did their shows anyway. Every year more and more performers came and in 1959 the Festival Fringe Society started.

D   The Society became formal and printed its own **programme** and sold tickets. The society lets anyone perform and doesn't check events before they start. Today it is the same – anyone with a story to tell and a place to perform can come.

READING

1   Read the text quickly. What is the text about?

a   Scottish music
b   Holidays in Scotland
c   A festival in Scotland

2   Read the text again and complete the sentences.

1   The Edinburgh Fringe Festival lasts for

_____.

2   The shows include comedy,

_____.

3   The first festival was in

_____.

4   The society lets anyone

_____.

3   Complete the sentences using words in bold from the text.

1   The _____ starts at 8pm every night.

2   The _____ includes music, dance and theatre.

3   There are many music _____ in England in the summer.

4   It's difficult to buy tickets for a show when the person is _____. Everyone wants to see them.

5   He _____ two shows every day for three weeks. He's very tired at the end.

GRAMMAR

PRESENT SIMPLE

1 **Correct the mistakes with the present simple in <u>five</u> of the sentences.**

1 People *comes* from all over the world for the Edinburgh Fringe Festival.

2 My parents *goes* to the festival every year.

3 We *stay* in a beautiful hotel in Edinburgh.

4 I *likes* the music best.

5 My brother *live* in Scotland.

6 The festival *lasts* for three weeks.

7 My cousins *visits* us for the festival.

8 Many visitors *want* to know about traditional Scottish food.

2 **Rewrite the sentences using the positive form.**

1 My parents don't like the festival.
   My parents like the festival.

2 A lot of tourists don't go to Edinburgh in August.
   _____

3 Most people don't enjoy music.
   _____

4 She doesn't eat meat.
   _____

5 The show doesn't start at 11:45.
   _____

6 Sally doesn't listen to traditional Scottish music.
   _____

7 I don't live near my family.
   _____

8 We don't have a holiday every year.
   _____

LISTENING

1 🔘8️⃣ **Listen to two students talking about Chinese New Year. Answer the questions.**

1 In which season does the Chinese New Year start?

2 How long does it last?

3 Which days are the most important?

2 Choose the correct answers.

1 In the UK, Chinese New Year is on *the same / a different* day every year.

2 People usually spend New Year with *family / friends*.

3 The New Year's Eve meal is traditionally *fish / meat*.

4 Children usually get money in *red / green* envelopes.

3 🔘8️⃣ **Listen again and check.**

Living IELTS

TALKING ABOUT LIKES AND DISLIKES

1 Read the table and write sentences about Paul and Katrina.

love	✓✓	don't like	✗
like	✓	hate	✗✗

	carnival	football	fish
Paul	✓✓	✓	✗✗
Katrina	✗	✓✓	✓

Paul loves carnival.

VOCABULARY

POSITIVE AND NEGATIVE ADJECTIVES

1 **Match the adjectives with the meanings.**

| 1 | awful | **a** | very bad or unpleasant |
| | amazing | **b** | very surprising or enjoyable |

| 2 | interesting | **a** | tastes very nice |
| | delicious | **b** | something you want to know more about |

| 3 | beautiful | **a** | not interesting |
| | boring | **b** | very pleasant or attractive |

| 4 | colourful | **a** | lots of different colours |
| | exciting | **b** | very interesting with lots happening |

| 5 | fantastic | **a** | very good |
| | freezing | **b** | very cold |

2 **Correct the adjectives in the sentences with adjectives in the box.**

> amazing   awful   colourful   boring   delicious

1 This carnival is *delicious*. The ones in my country are much bigger and more colourful.
2 Wow! Look at those floats. They're *boring*!
3 It's *exciting* celebrating New Year in Scotland. I hate the cold.
4 The parade is very *interesting*. The floats are very beautiful.
5 Can you show me how to cook this? It's *awful*.

PRONUNCIATION

SYLLABLE STRESS

1 **How many syllables are there in each of these words?**

1	amazing	_____
2	awful	_____
3	colourful	_____
4	boring	_____
5	fantastic	_____
6	exciting	_____

2 🔊⑨ **Listen again and check.**

3 🔊⑨ **Listen again. Circle the stressed syllables.**

GRAMMAR

PRESENT SIMPLE QUESTIONS AND SHORT ANSWERS

1 **Choose the correct questions.**

1   **a** Do you like the carnival?
    b Do you the carnival like?

2   **a** Do they celebrate New Year?
    b Do celebrate they New Year?

3   **a** Does take part she in the parade?
    b Does she take part in the parade?

4   **a** Does he visit his family in the holiday?
    b Does visit his family he in the holiday?

5   **a** Do I need a ticket?
    b Do I a ticket need?

6   **a** Do the fireworks you watch?
    b Do you watch the fireworks?

2 **Correct the mistakes in <u>three</u> of the questions.**

1   Do he speak Spanish?
2   Does she work?
3   Does they enjoy learning English?
4   Does we have homework?
5   Do your children watch TV?
6   Do I need my computer for the next lesson?

3 **Match the question words with the words below.**

> What   Where   When   How long

1   one day
2   5th November
3   England
4   Guy Fawkes Night

4 **Match the questions with the correct answers below.**

1   What do you like doing in your free time?
2   Where do you work?
3   What time does the restaurant open?
4   How long does your tutorial class last?
5   How much does a can of coke cost?

a   £1.50
b   I enjoy reading and watching TV.
c   In London.
d   Two hours.
e   At seven.

WRITING

DESCRIBING A FESTIVAL

1 Read the text and answer the questions.

1 When is May Day?
2 What happens on May Day?
3 What is May Day called in other countries?

2 Read the text again. Add the punctuation and the capital letters.

May Day

may day happens on the first of may in england it happens every year and it is traditionally celebrated at the end of winter. there is a may queen and traditional dancing. in oxford it is traditional to meet at 6 a.m. outside magdalen college. at durham university students enjoy folk dancing and traditional music it is called labour day in many other countries such as germany, bahrain and brazil.

WRITING SKILLS

PUNCTUATION

3 Complete the punctuation rules. Then check your answers to activity 2.

1 You use a ca __ __ t __ l l __ tt __ r at the beginning of a sentence.
2 You use a f __ __ l s __ __ p at the end of a sentence.
3 You use capital letters for the names of m __ __ th __, people, pl __ __ es, countries and special days.

4 Complete the text with the words in the box.

is happens remembers celebrate lasts

Guy Fawkes night ¹ _____ in winter in England. It ² _____ on the 5th November. It ³ _____ for one night. People ⁴ _____ by having a bonfire and fireworks. It ⁵ _____ the day Guy Fawkes and the gunpowder plot failed to blow up parliament in England.

UNDERSTANDING INSTRUCTIONS

(3min) Good language learners read instructions carefully because they know it's important to understand what an exercise or a test is about.

1 You have three minutes to answer the questions below. Quickly read all the questions first.

    1 Write four irregular English verbs.

    2 Circle the incorrect definition of the present continuous.
      a We use it for routines and habits.
      b We use it for things happening now.

    3 Circle the correct sentence.
      a I like fish.
      b I am liking fish.

    4 How many sections are there in the IELTS test?
      a 2   **b** 3   **c** 4

    5 What is the highest score in IELTS?
      a 7   **b** 8   **c** 9

    6 Write the numbers as words.
      a 101   **b** 888

    7 Put down your pen and relax. You do <u>not</u> need to answer any of the questions above.

2 Did you answer any of the questions in activity 1? If yes, read question 7 again.

3 Read the questions and example answers. What mistakes has the student made?

1 Complete the sentences using no more than three words.
You have to <u>listen to what your teacher says</u> carefully.

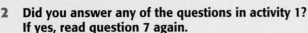

2 Choose the correct answer and write the appropriate letter in the space provided.
    A: In groups
    B: In pairs
    C: Individually   **Answer:** _In pairs_

3 Which one of the following best describes paragraph 2?
    i. Student life in England.
    ii. International students.
    iii. UK students overseas.   **Answer:** _i and ii_

4 Which two of the following are true?
    i. The restaurant opens at 8.
    ii. There isn't a free table.
    iii. The restaurant is near the station.
    Answer: _iii_

My goals

Set goals for yourself for this week. At the end of the week find out

1 how many different question types there are in the Reading and Listening tests.

2 what you have to do in each question type.

LISTENING SECTION 1

In Section 1 of the Listening test, you hear two people having a conversation in an everyday situation. For example, asking about travel arrangements, booking a course or asking for information.

1 Read the instructions from Section 1 and answer the questions.

> Listen to a man booking a course and complete the notes below. Write no more than three words and/or a number for each answer.
> 1 What is the situation? _____
> 2 How many words can you write for each question? _____
> 3 Can you write numbers? _____

2 Read the text and predict which type of questions you will hear in the conversation. Match the question words in the box with the gaps below.

> How much...?   How long ...?   When...?   What...?   Where...?

INTERNATIONAL BUSINESS COLLEGE – AVAILABLE COURSES:

Name of Course: 0 _Introduction to International Business_
Time: from 1 _____ to nine
Cost: free

COURSE CONTENT
• international work and local work
• cultural 2 _____
• common problems
Nearest Location: Cambridge
Next Course Date: 29th May

Name of course: 3 _____
Length of course: 4 _____
Cost: 5 _____ or £350 for the month

COURSE CONTENT
Week one: the European Union
Week two: transport
Weeks three and four: marketing and 6 _____
Nearest Location: Bury St Edmunds
Next Course Date: 29th May or 7 _____

CALLER'S DETAILS
Name: 8 _____
Address: 9 _____, Newmarket
Email: 10 _____

3 [CD 10] Listen and complete the text. Use your notes from activity 2 to help you.

4 At the end of the Listening test, you will have ten minutes to transfer your answers to an answer sheet. Poor spelling or grammar will lose marks. Circle the correct spellings below.

1 breif   ammount   accommodation
2 advertizement seperate   acceptable
3 envifament   techer   argument
4 calendar   beleive   benifit
5 colum   thier   until
6 relevant   skedule   pronounciation

5 Correct the words in activity 4. Use your dictionary to help you.

Exam Tip

Complete the tips using the words in the box.

> spelling   instructions   type   number

1 Read the _____ carefully.
2 Check the _____ of words you can use.
3 Predict the _____ of information you will hear.
4 Check your answers for correct _____.

Teamwork

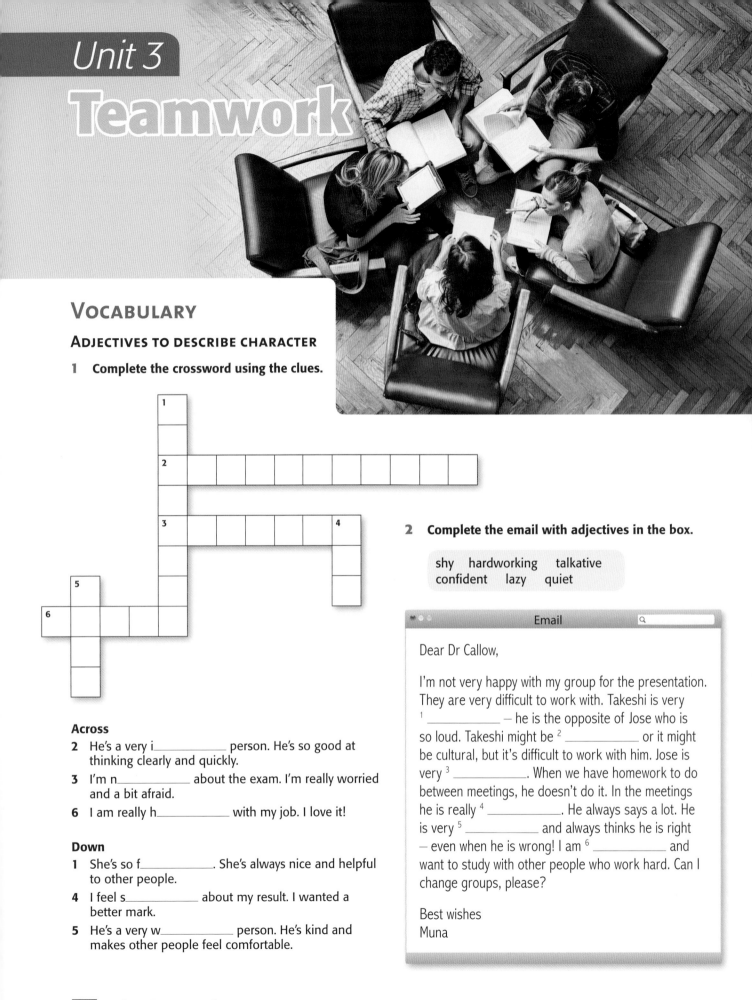

VOCABULARY

ADJECTIVES TO DESCRIBE CHARACTER

1 **Complete the crossword using the clues.**

Across

2 He's a very i_____ person. He's so good at thinking clearly and quickly.

3 I'm n_____ about the exam. I'm really worried and a bit afraid.

6 I am really h_____ with my job. I love it!

Down

1 She's so f_____. She's always nice and helpful to other people.

4 I feel s_____ about my result. I wanted a better mark.

5 He's a very w_____ person. He's kind and makes other people feel comfortable.

2 **Complete the email with adjectives in the box.**

> shy   hardworking   talkative
> confident   lazy   quiet

Email

Dear Dr Callow,

I'm not very happy with my group for the presentation. They are very difficult to work with. Takeshi is very ¹ _____ — he is the opposite of Jose who is so loud. Takeshi might be ² _____ or it might be cultural, but it's difficult to work with him. Jose is very ³ _____. When we have homework to do between meetings, he doesn't do it. In the meetings he is really ⁴ _____. He always says a lot. He is very ⁵ _____ and always thinks he is right — even when he is wrong! I am ⁶ _____ and want to study with other people who work hard. Can I change groups, please?

Best wishes
Muna

LISTENING

1 [CD 11] **Listen to three students planning a presentation and complete the notes.**

Presentation topic: _____

Presentation date: _____

Date of meeting: _____

2 [CD 11] **Listen again and match the person with what they can do.**

1	Max	a	I can use IT well.
2	Theo	b	I can work alone well.
3	Zara	c	I can speak confidently in front of other people.

GRAMMAR

ADVERBS OF FREQUENCY

1 **Put the adverbs of frequency in order.**

often   sometimes   usually   never   always

1 _____   3 often   5 _____

0% ←——————|——————|——————|——————→ 100%

2 _____   4 _____

2 **Put the adverbs of frequency in brackets in the correct position in the sentences.**

1 We have to work in teams at university. (often)
2 I give presentations. (sometimes)
3 The lecturers give us a test at the end of the year. (usually)
4 We have a multiple choice test. It is essays. (never, always)

3 **Complete the sentences with the name of a person you know.**

1 _____ is very hardworking. He studies a lot.
2 My friend, _____, is the most talkative person I know.
3 My classmate, _____, is quite shy.
4 The most confident person I know is _____.
5 _____ is lazy. He doesn't do any work.
6 _____ is very quiet.

3 **Complete the sentences with the adverb described in brackets.**

1 I _____ make mistakes in English. (quite a lot, but not all the time)
2 I _____ miss my Monday morning nine o'clock class. (every week)
3 We _____ have to work in groups. (not very often)
4 My tutor _____ gives us homework. (nearly every class)
5 I _____ arrive late for class. (not one time)

READING

1 **Read the text quickly and choose the correct answers.**

1 ... think group work is a good idea.
   a Lecturers
   b Students

2 Group work can be difficult because ...
   a people work in different ways.
   b some people are always wrong.

3 Group work is best when ...
   a everyone can do what they want.
   b everything is planned and organised well.

2 **Replace the definitions in the sentences with the words in bold from the text.**

1 She always tries to *control* the group.
2 The meetings are difficult, but it helps me to *improve* my English.
3 His *job* in the group is to research the topic.
4 We *tell each other* opinions on a topic in our meetings.
5 We need a *list of all the things we have to do*.

Students often have to work in groups at university. This is because many lecturers think there are advantages to group work. You can **share** your ideas and find solutions to problems. You can **develop** your communication skills. You can also learn about different cultures and improve your English.

However, there are problems with working in a group. Sometimes a very confident or talkative person can **dominate** the group. Some group members never speak – they just sit in silence. Sometimes people only want to talk and not listen. This might be because they think they are right and they think everyone else is wrong.

Students can avoid these kinds of problems by making rules. For example, agree **an agenda** for the meeting and how often the group will meet. Always agree the deadlines for the work. Usually it is helpful for everyone to have a **role**. For example, one person takes notes, another does research, and another produces the PowerPoint slides.

Doing group work at university is an important experience that you also need for your future.

VOLUNTEER IN COSTA RICA

An exciting opportunity to work for the summer in Costa Rica. You can help local farms in village communities. Help people to change how they farm, so they can protect local plants and animals.

We need people who:
- are good at working in teams.
- have an excellent ability to communicate.
- have the ability to speak another language.

If possible, they should also:
- have a full driving licence.
- have experience of leading a team.

DO YOU HAVE THE SKILLS WE NEED?
Contact us at
vol.costarica@gmail.com

GRAMMAR

CAN / CAN'T FOR ABILITY

1 **Read the advert and complete the notes with *can* or *can't*.**

The company ...
1 wants people who _____ work in teams.
2 doesn't want shy people and people who _____ communicate.
3 wants people who _____ speak languages.
4 wants people who _____ drive.
5 doesn't want people who _____ lead others.

2 **Read the table and decide who is best for the job.**

	work in a team	good communication	language skills	drive	leading a team
Beth	✗	✓	✗	✓	✗
Ciara	✓	✓	✓	✗	✓
Vera	✓	✗	✓	✗	✗

3 **Complete the text using your answers from activities 1 and 2.**

¹ _____ is the best candidate for the volunteer job. She ² _____ work in a team and ³ _____ communicate well with others. She ⁴ _____ speak another language. She ⁵ _____ drive, but she ⁶ _____ lead a team well.

Reading

1 Read the letters and answer these questions.

1 Who is studying Chemistry? _____
2 Who volunteers in a school? _____
3 Who lives in Italy? _____
4 Who works with homeless people? _____
5 Who speaks at least three languages? _____
6 Who leads a group every week? _____

Hi

I'm interested in taking part in the Volunteer in Costa Rica programme. I'm a student at the University of Melbourne in Australia. My degree is in Business and Management and I'm in my second year. I want to get more experience of working in teams.
In my degree I often work in teams to give presentations and sometimes lead the group. I also volunteer at a school in Melbourne. I can speak Italian, Greek and English and I help students from these countries when their English isn't very good.
I'm very hardworking and hope I can take part in the volunteer programme.

Best wishes
Anastasia

Hi

I'm writing to you about the Volunteer in Costa Rica programme. I'm a student at the University of Milan in Italy. My degree is in Chemistry and I'm in my final year.

I also work as a volunteer for a charity in Milan. I lead a team of volunteers who help homeless people. This is my third year working for the charity and my first year leading a group. Four nights a week our team drives to different parts of Milan to give food and clothes to homeless people.

I can speak Italian and English. Speaking English helps me to communicate because some homeless people can't speak Italian.

I love helping people and I hope you can use my skills in Costa Rica.

Kind Regards
Giuseppe

2 There is only one more place in the Volunteer in Costa Rica programme on page 23. Who is the best person for the job, Anastasia or Giuseppe? Why?

Pronunciation

Strong and weak forms: *Can* and *Can't*

1 [12] Listen to Georgios and Omar talking about what they can and can't do. Tick the things they can do.

	Georgios	Omar
speak Spanish		
use a computer		
drive		
work under pressure		
work in a team		

2 [13] Listen and choose the correct pronunciation of *can*.

1 *strong / weak*   3 *strong / weak*
2 *strong / weak*   4 *strong / weak*

Living IELTS

Talking about ability

1 Complete the sentences for you. Use *I can* or *I can't*.

1 _____ speak Spanish.
2 _____ use a computer.
3 _____ drive.
4 _____ work under pressure.
5 _____ work in a team

2 Say the sentences in activity 1 and practise your pronunciation of *can* and *can't*.

WRITING

DESCRIBING A GOOD LEADER

1 **Read the text and answer the questions.**

  1 Do good leaders understand everything about their job?

  2 Do good leaders talk a lot? Why/ Why not?

  3 What three skills do good leaders need?

> Good leaders in the workplace are confident and they are good at their job. They have a lot of work experience and they understand everything about their job too. Employees then have confidence in the leader and trust them. Good leaders also have good communication skills. This doesn't mean talking a lot – it means listening to employees. A leader makes decisions all the time and it is important that the decisions are good.

WRITING SKILLS

LINKING IDEAS WITH *AND*, *TOO* AND *ALSO*

2 **Read the text again and answer the questions.**

  1 Which word usually joins two ideas together?

  2 Which <u>two</u> words are used to add an idea?

  3 Which word do we usually put at the end of a sentence?

3 **Complete the text with *and*, *too* and *also*.**

Some people think leaders _____ managers are different. Managers make simple decisions but leaders _____ motivate people to work hard. Leaders don't only make decisions – people want to follow them _____.

4 **Correct the mistakes with *and*, *too* and *also* in the sentences.**

  1 Tayo is warm *too* friendly.

  2 Helen is kind. She is *too* generous.

  3 Lucia is honest *also* hardworking.

  4 Paul is intelligent. He is funny *and*.

UNDERSTANDING THE IELTS TEST

Preparing well for any test is important. Find out everything you can about the format of the IELTS test and what happens in the different tests.

1 **Choose the correct answers to describe the IELTS test.**

1 There are *three / four* different tests in IELTS.

2 In the Writing test, you have to write *an essay / a story* or describe a graph, table, chart or diagram.

3 There are four sections in the Listening test. You listen to *monologues, dialogues and conversations with up to *three / four* people.

4 There are *three / four* reading passages in the Reading test.

5 There are three parts in the speaking test – questions on everyday topics, a long individual turn and *a two-way discussion / a presentation*.

*monologue = one person talking

2 🔘14 **Listen to two students discussing the IELTS practice test they did yesterday. Complete the advice below.**

Listening

1 You should _____ the questions for the next section during the test.

2 You should _____ your answers to the answer sheet at the end of the test.

2 You should _____ the instructions carefully.

Reading

4 You shouldn't _____ too long on one question.

5 You shouldn't _____ more words than you're allowed.

Writing

6 You shouldn't use personal _____ – it makes it sound informal.

7 You should _____ words correctly.

Speaking

8 You should give _____ answers.

9 You should answer all the _____ on the task card.

My goals

Complete the table with things you want to find out about the IELTS test.

Section	Things to find out
Writing	What types of things do I have to describe in the first writing task?
Reading	
Listening	
Speaking	

READING STRATEGY 1

In the Reading test, you read different types of texts and answer different types of questions. You can read the questions first or you can read the text first. Choose the technique that helps you.

1 Read the text first and then answer the questions below.

A The University of Bologna in Italy is a popular place to study. Over 100 000 students study there today. No one knows when it first opened, but most people believe it was probably in 1088.

B The university was started when groups of French, English and other foreign students decided to form a university. So the University of Bologna was also probably the first international university in the world.

C Today the University of Bologna is one of the best 200 universities in the world. It has centres in five Italian cities and a centre in Buenos Aires, the capital city of Argentina.

1 … when the university opened.
  a Everyone knows   **b** No one knows

2 … students started the university.
  a Italian   **b** International

3 The university has centres in … .
  a two countries
  b only Italy

2 Now read the questions first and then read the text below to answer the questions.

1 A university … the only place you can get a degree.
  a is   **b** isn't

2 They are offering a degree in … .
  a Food Science   **b** Managing Business

3 … can do this course.
  a All employees
  b Only managers

A There are over 12 000 universities around the world offering degrees, but a university is not the only place you can get a degree. The fast-food giant McDonald's has also started to offer degree courses.

B In the UK, McDonalds is now offering a two-year foundation degree in Managing Business. The company pays the tuition fees. In its first year, there were 53 employees on the degree course.

C Not all McDonalds employees can do the degree – they have to get a job as a manager first. However, as degree courses are very expensive, school leavers may prefer a job and a degree with McDonalds.

3 Which technique did you think was easier: reading the text first or reading the questions first? Tick the comments below you agree with.

> I prefer to read the text quickly first just to understand the topic.

> I think it's better to read the questions first. Then you can find the information quicker.

> Reading the text first helps me feel confident about answering the questions.

> I like reading the questions first. They are in the same order as the text, so the questions help me understand the text as I read.

4 In activity 1, the answers are in the text in the order below:

question 1 = paragraph a   question 2 = paragraph b
question 3 = paragraph c

Read the text in activity 2 again. Do the questions and answers follow the order of the text?

Exam Tip

Complete the tips using the words in the box.

> questions   order   text   technique

1 Practise reading the questions first and then reading the text first. Decide which _____ is best for you.

2 Reading the _____ first can help you find answers quickly.

3 Reading the _____ first can help you understand the general meaning.

4 Remember that the questions often follow the _____ of the text.

Unit 4
Education

VOCABULARY

ACADEMIC SUBJECTS AND HIGHER EDUCATION

1 **Complete the academic subjects.**

1 G __ __ lo __ __
2 L __ __ erat __ __ e
3 M __ __ __ s
4 C __ __ pu __ __ __ Sc __ __ nc __
5 Bu __ __ __ es __
6 L __ __
7 E __ __ in __ __ __ ing
8 M __ __ ic __ __ e
9 __ __ __ gua __ __ __ __
10 __ ocio __ __ __ y
11 P __ __ __ ho __ __ gy
12 B __ __ log __

2 **Complete the sentences with words from activity 1.**

1 I like _____ because I like learning about animals and plants.

2 I like studying _____ because I love reading.

3 I don't like _____, but I'm good with numbers.

4 So many people study _____ but I think working is better to get many jobs in a company.

5 _____ is about the study of society.

6 _____ is the study of the mind.

7 I enjoy studying _____. My favourite is English.

8 In _____ we study rocks, volcanoes and minerals.

9 Today we learnt about the micro-chip in _____.

10 Contract and criminal _____ are two of our modules.

11 I am studying _____ because I want to work in construction.

12 I am studying _____ to become a doctor.

3 **Complete the words and phrases about education in these sentences.**

1 University and college is sometimes called h__ __her e __ __ __ __ at __ on.

2 When you finish at university you get a d __ g __ __ __ __.

3 Your record at university is called a q __ __ __ ific __ __ __ __ __ n.

4 When you do well in a test you p __ __ __.

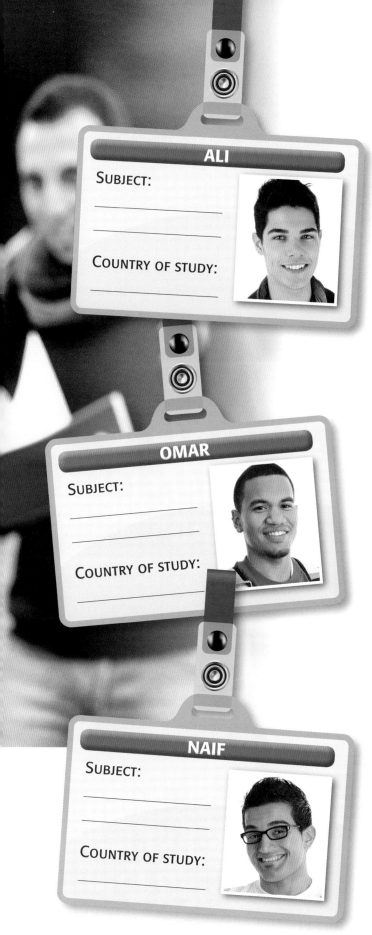

LISTENING

STUDYING ABROAD

1. **Read activity 2 below and answer these questions.**
   1. Who are you going to listen to?
   2. Where are they going to be speaking?
   3. What are they going to speak about?
   4. What information do you need to listen for?

2. 🔘 15 **Ali, Omar and Naif are studying at university. Now they are going back to their school to talk about their experience. What subject are they studying and in which country?**

3. 🔘 15 **Listen again. Circle the things each person does in their free time.**

   Ali
   1. work in shop
   2. play football
   3. study
   4. go shopping

   Omar
   1. meet friends
   2. eat out
   3. surf the net
   4. work

   Naif
   1. go shopping
   2. go walking
   3. study a postgraduate course
   4. go to Sydney

PRONUNCIATION

SYLLABLE STRESS

1. **Put the words in the box into the correct column for syllable stress.**

   geology   literature   languages   sociology
   psychology   biology

Ooo	oOoo	ooOoo

2. 🔘 16 **Listen and check. Then listen again and repeat the words.**

GRAMMAR

PRESENT CONTINUOUS

1 Read the audioscript for track 15 on page 102 and underline examples of the present continuous.

2 Saif is another student presenting today. Make sentences to complete Saif's presentation notes using the present continuous.

   1 study / computer science / at Southampton University

     <u>I am studying computer science at Southampton University.</u>

   2 do / a three year undergraduate course

   3 take / French

   4 hope / to spend the summer in France

   5 think / of renting a house next year

   6 look / for a house at the moment

3 Write questions in the present continuous to ask to Ali, Omar, Naif and Saif.

Questions for Ali

   1 <u>who / live / with?</u>

   2 <u>you / work / hard?</u>

Questions for Omar

   3 <u>you / like / live / in Australia?</u>

   4 <u>what / modules / you / study / for Sociology?</u>

Questions for Naif

   5 <u>why / hope / to study a postgraduate course?</u>

Questions for Saif

   6 <u>you / enjoy / living with British students?</u>

4 Match your questions 1–6 with the correct answer below.

   a I love living with British students – it's great for my English!

   b I'm not working that hard, but the second year is harder.

   c I'm studying culture, society and politics.

   d I'm living with my friend Ahmed.

   e I love living there.

   f I'm hoping to work in a university.

READING

BRITISH STUDENTS ABROAD

1 (3min) **Read the text in three minutes and answer these questions.**

   1 Is the number of British students studying overseas decreasing?

   2 What percentage of British students study overseas?

   3 Which country is the most popular for British students?

   4 What is the Erasmus programme?

   5 How many students take part in the Erasmus programme?

A People often think of international students as students from around the world studying in countries such as the UK, the USA or Australia. However, there are also a growing number of British students going to study overseas.

Abroad: in or to a foreign country.
My cousin is living abroad. Do you want to study abroad?

2 **Read the text again and answer these questions.**

1 What do most people think about international students?
2 Do more Chinese, British or Indian students study abroad?
3 How many British students are there in France?
4 Where does the Erasmus programme happen?

3 **Complete the sentences with the words in the box.**

> western   campuses   global   overseas

1 Many students go to a _____ style university to help get a better job when they go back home.
2 Many companies are not local but _____ and have offices in many countries.
3 People who work for international companies often have to work _____ for some time.
4 Large companies come to university _____ to find the best students to work in their company.

B Surprisingly, as a percentage, more British students are travelling abroad than students from other countries. 1.7 per cent of the entire British student population is studying abroad. This percentage is higher than China at 1.4 per cent and India at 1 per cent of their student population.

C There are over 22 000 British students studying in different parts of the world. The three most popular countries for British students are the USA (8 500), France (2 600) and Germany (2 200).

D One popular study abroad programme for British students is the Erasmus programme that allows European students to spend a year in another European country. The number of British students taking part in the programme is increasing every year. Now over 10 000 take part annually in the programme. Perhaps British students are becoming more global.

PRONUNCIATION

NUMBERS

1 ⊙ 17 **Listen and circle the numbers, a or b.**

1	**a** 1.4	**b** 4
2	**a** 1.7	**b** 7
3	**a** 2 200	**b** 22 000
4	**a** 1.2	**b** 2.1
5	**a** 6.3	**b** 63
6	**a** 12 000	**b** 1 200

2 ⊙ 18 **Listen and repeat. Practise saying the numbers below.**

> 1.8   8 500   800   2.7   2 600
> 1 800   2.3   150   15 280

Grammar

Present continuous and present simple

1 **Choose the correct verbs to complete these sentences.**

1 My cousin *studies / is studying* maths in Bristol at the moment.
2 More than 22 000 British students *are studying / study* abroad this year.
3 Nearly 200 000 students *take / are taking* part in Erasmus this year.
4 Many British people *go / are going* to the USA to study.
5 I *am living / live* in Germany for the summer.
6 British children usually *learn / are learning* French at school.

2 **Match the charts to these descriptions. Then complete the descriptions with the words below. Use the present continuous form of the verbs below.**

go up   go down   stay the same

1 The number of people going to university _____.
2 The number of universities _____.
3 The number of courses in English _____.

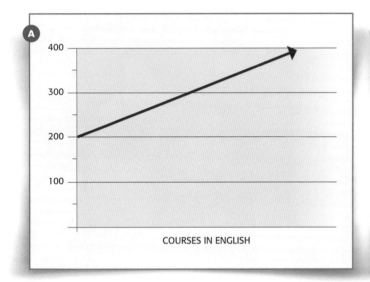

A COURSES IN ENGLISH

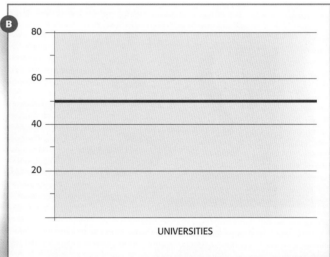

B UNIVERSITIES

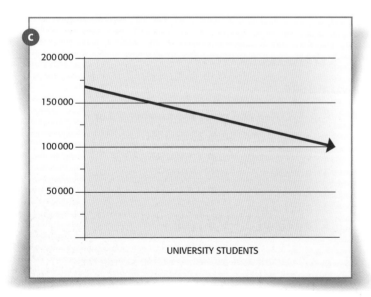

C UNIVERSITY STUDENTS

WRITING

DESCRIBING GRAPHS

1 Read the chart below and choose the best words to complete the description.

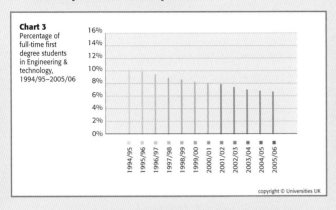

The ¹ *bar chart / line graph* shows the percentage of students studying Engineering and technology in the UK. On the left we can see the percentage of students and on the bottom we can see the time in years. The percentage of students is ² *increasing / going down* every year. This shows that Engineering and technology is ³ *less / more* popular.

WRITING SKILLS

DESCRIBING TRENDS

2 Read the graph and complete the text with the phrases in the box.

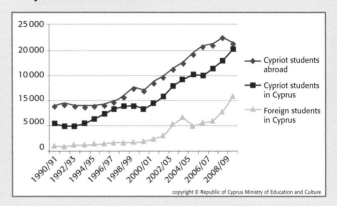

> is becoming   line graph   On the left
> is increasing

The ¹ _____ shows the number of international students in Cyprus.
² _____, we can see the number of students and on the bottom we can see the time in years. The number of foreign students in Cyprus ³ _____. This shows that Cyprus ⁵ _____ a popular country for international students.

3 Read the graph and complete the text.

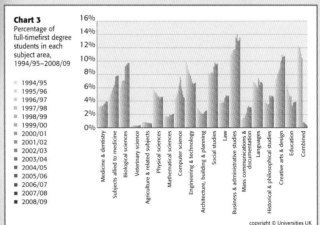

The ¹ _____ shows the percentage of students in the UK studying ² _____. On the left, we can see the ³ _____ and at the bottom we can see the ⁴ _____. The number of students studying Business and Administration ⁵ _____.This shows that Business and Administration ⁶ _____ a popular subject to study in the UK.

IMPROVING YOUR VOCABULARY 1

Good language learners keep a vocabulary notebook. It's impossible to learn all the new words you see, so you need to decide which words you want to learn. You also need to have good techniques to learn them.

1 **Answer the questions. Write your answers in your vocabulary notebook.**

   1 Write three reasons why you decide to learn a new word.
     <u>I'm interested in sport so when I see words about sport I like to write them down.</u>

   2 Write four things you can do when you see or hear a word you don't understand.
     _____

   3 Write three techniques you use to revise vocabulary.
     _____

   4 Write five things that are important to learn about new words.
     _____

2 **Read the extract from a vocabulary notebook. Are the ideas similar to your answers in activity 1 number 4 above?**

Word formation	Example sentence	Translation	Pronunciation	*Collocation
globalise (v) globalisation (n) global (adj) globally (adv)	British students are becoming more global.	عالمي	/ˈgləʊbəl/	global problem

*****Collocation:** words that often go together.

3 **Read the text on pages 32–33 again. Underline any new words or phrases. Do you think these words and phrases are important to learn? Why? Why not?**

4 **Choose four important words or phrases from activity 3 and add them to the table in activity 2. Complete the information about each new word and phrase.**

My goals

1 Buy a vocabulary notebook or create a new document on your computer. Make a table similar to the one in activity 2 and add all new vocabulary to it for the next two weeks.

2 Read your notes again after two weeks and check how many new words you know. You can also compare notes with a classmate and test each other.

WRITING TASK 1

In Section 1 of the Writing test, you describe different types of visual information. These can include a table, a chart or a graph. It's important to understand the differences.

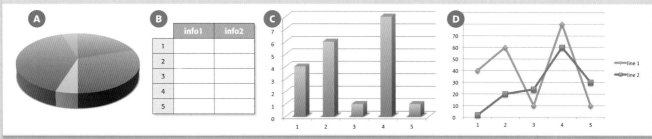

1 Look at the different types of visual information. Which one is a …

1 bar chart? **3** line graph?

2 pie chart? **4** table?

2 Read the two charts and answer the questions.

A: Internet shoppers by age group

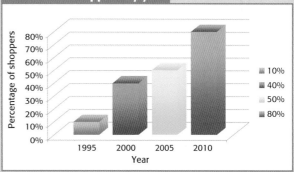

B: Internet shoppers by year

1 What information does chart A show?

2 What do the colours represent in chart A?

3 Which axis shows the percentage of internet shoppers in chart B?

4 How many years are in chart B?

3 Match the descriptions with a chart in activity 2.

1 Not many people shopped on the internet in 1995. The number is increasing every year. Between 2000 and 2005 the number is going up. From 2005 to 2010 the number is growing quickly.

2 The chart shows the number of shoppers on the internet by age group. More people aged 18-24 use the internet than the 65+ group. The number is the same in the 25-34 group and the 35-44 group.

4 Put the words in the box into the correct group.

> increasing decreasing growing
> falling rising

going up	going down

Exam Tip

Complete the tips using the words in the box.

> trends important type

1 Identify the _____ of visual information.

2 Find the _____ information such as the title and each axis.

3 Look for patterns and _____ and think of a useful word you can use.

Unit 5
Buildings and cities

VOCABULARY

ADJECTIVES TO DESCRIBE BUILDINGS

1 **Complete the sentences with the words in the box.**

> glass   ugly   modern   tall

1 _____ buildings, like skyscrapers, often have a lot of _____ outside and this means that window cleaners have a lot more work!

2 Some people prefer _____ buildings to old buildings. They don't like the design of the old ones and they think they are _____.

> unusual   fantastic   brick   wonderful

3 Many people think the Barcelona Olympic stadium is _____ and _____, but others think it is ugly.

4 The Chrysler building was the world's tallest _____ and steel building. It is made from over 3 million bricks.

5 The Basket building in Ohio is really _____. It looks like a huge shopping basket and there's not another building in the world like it.

2 **Match the words in the box with pictures A, B and C.**

> old   stone   glass   ugly   modern
> concrete   tall   huge   unusual
> fantastic   small   brick   wonderful

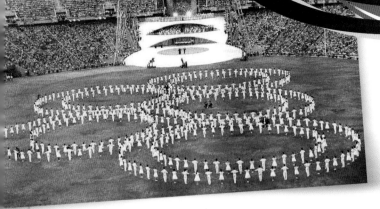

The Olympics and Barcelona

A The Olympics are a major international sports event. It happens every two years in the summer and then in the winter.

B Many countries want to host the Olympics, but it is a very difficult event to organise. Countries have to *construct new buildings and make old buildings more modern. However, it can give an old city a new life and improve the city. It can also make a lot of money. Atlanta, Georgia, in the USA, made $300 million from the 2004 Olympics.

C The Spanish city of Barcelona is more than 2 000 years old. It has many fantastic old buildings and is famous for the architect, Gaudi. His unusual stone and brick buildings are all across the city. Since the 1992 Olympics, you can also see many modern buildings in the city.

D The Olympic port was an ugly, old area of Barcelona. There wasn't a nice beach in the city, but now there is a wonderful man-made beach. Before the Olympics, there were many huge, ugly concrete and glass hotels. Construction workers made the old hotels more modern. Today Barcelona is the twelfth most visited city in the world!

*construct = build

READING

1 **What do you know about the Olympics and the city of Barcelona? Choose T (true) or F (false).**

1	The Olympics are a major sports event.	T / F
2	The Olympics happen every four years.	T / F
3	The Olympics always happen in the summer.	T / F
4	The Olympics usually loses money for the host city.	T / F
5	A lot of construction happens for most Olympics.	T / F
6	Barcelona is in Spain.	T / F
7	Barcelona is an historic city.	T / F
8	There was a lot of construction for the Barcelona Olympics.	T / F
9	The Barcelona Olympics were a success.	T / F
10	Tourists think Barcelona is a wonderful city.	T / F

2 **Read the text and check your answers.**

3 **Choose the correct answers.**

1 The Summer Olympics happen every …
  a two years.
  b four years.

2 The Olympics are usually …
  a good for a city.
  b bad for a city.

3 Gaudi is …
  a a building.
  b an architect.

4 The Olympic port is now …
  a a modern area.
  b an ugly area.

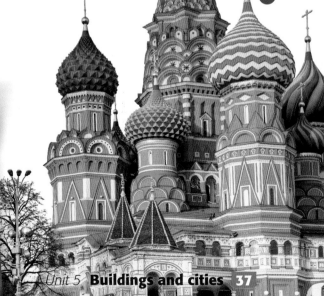

Grammar

Past simple of *be*

1 Read the text opposite and answer the questions.

1 When was the first modern Olympics?
2 When were women first allowed to compete?
3 How many countries were at the Athens Olympics?
4 Where was the most expensive opening ceremony?

2 Complete the text with *was, wasn't, were* or *weren't.*

3 Rewrite the sentences in the negative form.

1 The 2004 Athens Olympics were a success.
  _____

2 I was at home yesterday.
  _____

3 We were on holiday last week.
  _____

4 He was ill on Monday.
  _____

5 The city was very modern.
  _____

6 The athletes were very happy.
  _____

4 Complete the sentences using the positive (✔) or negative (✗) forms.

1 I _____ (✔) at work last night. I _____ (✗) at home.
2 She _____ (✗) ill on Monday. She _____ (✔) on holiday.
3 They _____ (✗) here at the weekend. They _____ (✔) at their parents'.
4 The hotel _____ (✗) very nice. It _____ (✔) too old.

5 Complete the questions. Then match the questions with the answers in activity 4.

1 Where _____ she on Monday?
2 What _____ the hotel like?
3 Where _____ you last night?
4 Where _____ they at the weekend?

The modern Olympics

ATHENS

Athens [1] _____ the city to host the first modern Olympics in 1896. There [2] _____ 14 countries at the Olympics and there were 241 athletes and 43 events in total. In 1900 the Olympics [3] _____ in Paris. There [4] _____ (not) a stadium for these Olympics, but it was an important event because it [5] _____ the first time women could compete.

There [6] _____ (not) any opening ceremonies until 1920 when the first one [7] _____ in Antwerp. The 1984 Los Angeles Olympics [8] _____ the first Olympics to make a lot of money (US$225 million). In 2004 the Olympics [9] _____ in Athens again, but this time there [10] _____ over 10 000 athletes from over 200 countries. In 2008 the opening ceremony in Beijing [11] _____ one of the most expensive ever, costing $100 million.

LISTENING

1 🔘 19 **Listen to Ibrahim and Ming. Choose true (T) or false (F).**

1	Ibrahim and Ming study together.	T / F
2	The builders finished the stadium in 2003.	T / F
3	Ibrahim likes the design.	T / F
4	1 700 builders worked on it.	T / F
5	It cost more than planned.	T / F

2 **Match the information with the numbers.**

1	started building	a	200 million
2	finished building	b	2008
3	number of workers	c	2003
4	money saved	d	17 000

3 🔘 19 **Listen again and check.**

GRAMMAR

PAST SIMPLE: REGULAR VERBS

1 Complete the text with the correct form of the verbs.

The designer of the National Stadium in Beijing created a very special design for this Olympic venue. People [1] _____ (call) the National Stadium 'The Bird's Nest Stadium', because it [2] _____ (look) like a bird's nest. Why a bird's nest? In China, there is a traditional soup made from bird's nests. The soup was expensive because it [3] _____ (need) real bird's nests. The designer [4] _____ (believe) the bird's nest was a good idea for a special sports event.

2 Complete the text using the past simple form of the verbs in the box.

> travel   need   call   work   hate   believe   ask

I [1] _____ school, but I love university! When I was at school I [2] _____ five miles on a bus every day. Here I get up five minutes before class and walk across campus. At school we [3] _____ to do homework every day. The teachers [4] _____ we should remember everything. When they [5] _____ out your name they [6] _____ you lots of questions. I [7] _____ really hard every night. At university I have to work hard, but they want us to think and have an opinion. It's great!

3 Choose the correct sentence.

1. **a** I don't go to work last week.
   b I didn't go to work last week.

2. **a** The project didn't finish on time.
   b The project don't finish on time.

3. **a** We didn't have lunch.
   b We no have lunch.

4. **a** They doesn't stop work until midnight.
   b They didn't stop work until midnight.

5. **a** I didn't have an English class yesterday.
   b I don't have an English class yesterday.

PRONUNCIATION

1 🔊 20 Listen and tick the pronunciation of the -ed ending of the verbs.

		/t/	/ɪd/	/d/
1	arrived			
2	needed			
3	stopped			
4	started			
5	watched			
6	used			
7	worked			

2 🔊 20 Listen again and repeat the words.

Living IELTS

BEING POSITIVE

Complete the expressions.

1. I love my city. It's a really sp__ __t__c__l__r city.
2. It looks a__ __ __ __g in at night with all the lights and the tall buildings.
3. It also looks very d__ __ __ __ __ __c at night because there are lights on the castle and in the old town.
4. It's d__ __ __ __ __ __ __ly my favourite city in the whole world.

💬 comments (1)   ◁ Share   👍 like (230)   🐦 follow us   ✉ send to a friend

Lisbon

Lisbon is the [1]_____ of Portugal. It is on the River Tagus, about half way down the country's coast. It is a [2]_____ city with a [3]_____ of 500 000. It is a [4]_____ city, but there are many modern developments. It was the home of the European Football Championships 2004 and it was also the Expo City in 1998. The city [5]_____ has got a [6]_____ nightlife and excellent shopping in the day.

It's a fantastic place to visit.

WRITING

DESCRIBING A CITY

1 **Read the text above and answer the questions.**

    1 Where is Lisbon?
    2 How many people live there?
    3 When were the European Championships?
    4 When was Lisbon the Expo City?

2 **Read the text again and complete it with words in the box.**

> historical   lively   medium-sized
> capital city   population   centre

3 **Complete the sentences with three words from activity 2 and information about your country.**

_____ is the [1]_____ of my country.
It is a [2]_____ city with a population of
_____.
The city [3]_____ has got _____.

WRITING SKILLS

ORGANISING A PARAGRAPH

4 **Read the description of Cologne. Put the sentences in the order below:**

    1 the name of the city and its main characteristics
    2 the location of the city
    3 the size of the city
    4 the main industries
    5 when it hosted the World Cup

> It is a large city with a population of more than one million. The main industries are insurance and media. In 2006, Cologne was one of the German cities to host the World Cup. The city is on the River Rhine, in the west of Germany. Cologne is a modern and lively city.

CULTURAL DIFFERENCES

International students are not only studying new courses, they are sometimes studying in a new city and a new country. It's important to learn about cultural and educational differences.

1 Look at the photos of different cultures and different places. What differences can you see? Think about the words in the box below.

> food   people   clothes   shops

2 When you study and live in a different culture, there are different rules about how to behave. Read the situations and circle the answer for you.

1 Today is Wednesday. You have an essay to finish for Monday and your parents are visiting you on Friday. Your parents want you to show them round your new town. What would you do?

   a Ask your teacher for a later deadline.

   b Miss the class.

   c Tell your parents to go out on their own.

2 You arrive 15 minutes late for a lecture. What do you do?

   a Go straight to the lecturer and apologise.

   b Go in quietly and try not to be noticed.

   c Wait outside and apologise afterwards.

3 Your teacher gives you lots of reading to do between classes but never checks that you have read the texts. You find them very difficult. What do you do?

   a Stop reading the texts. They can't be important because the teacher never checks.

   b Keep reading because you are responsible for your learning and education.

   c Only read the easy texts or easy parts of the text.

3 Imagine your lecturer is a professor, *Professor John Paulson*. What do you call him?

1 John		**5** Mr Paulson
2 Mate		**6** Dr Paulson
3 Sir		**7** Mr John
4 Prof		**8** Teacher

4 Compare your answers with a classmate from another country. What did you learn about another culture?

EDUCATIONAL DIFFERENCES

1 **Match the words with the definitions below.**

1	postgraduate	**a**	An interactive class for a smaller group of students.
2	seminar	**b**	A lecturer presenting information to students.
3	lecture	**c**	There are two or three of these every year.
4	semester	**d**	A short course of study that is part of a subject.
5	module	**e**	The next degree you take after your first degree.

2 **Read the statements. Choose T (true) or F (false) for your current experience of education. Make the false statements true for you.**

1	Lectures often have between 50 and 300 people.	T / F
2	In seminars, students only listen to the teacher.	T / F
3	You can ask lots of questions in a lecture.	T / F
4	A mark over 60% is good.	T / F
5	Most students do not live with their family.	T / F
6	You must go to lectures.	T / F
7	Most postgraduate courses usually have three semesters.	T / F
8	Students do presentations for many modules.	T / F

My goals

Think about your experience of school and university. What differences did/will you experience? Complete the table below.

At school	At university
The teachers set and check lots of work. I listened to the teacher and I didn't speak.	I need to take responsibility for my own learning. I need to speak and give my opinion in seminars.

Work

VOCABULARY

WORK

1 **Choose the correct noun to complete the collocation.**

1 I work as *a job / a volunteer*.

2 I need to work *full time / new skills* to make enough money.

3 I want to apply for *a job / experience* I saw in the newspaper.

4 I want to get *a volunteer / experience* in the summer holidays.

5 I am *full time / well-paid* at the moment so I can buy everything I want.

6 I want to develop *new skills / well-paid* to improve my CV.

2 **Complete the text using nouns from activity 1.**

I want to apply for a ¹ _____ I saw on the internet, but I also want to work as a ² _____ for a charity. The volunteer job will help me develop ³ _____ and I can get a better job after university. In the volunteer position I will have to work ⁴ _____, so there won't be any time to do any other work – but I need money. I think I want a ⁵ _____ job. So do I get ⁶ _____ or make money?

LISTENING

1 🔊 **21** **Listen to two friends talking. What is the conversation about?**

1 Their favourite food.

2 Being a student.

3 A module they want to do.

4 A friend they both know.

2 🔊 **21** **Listen again and choose the correct answers.**

1 Where did Leandro go this morning?
He went to *lectures / a talk*.

2 Did Geraldine enjoy the module?
Yes, she did. / No, she didn't.

3 What did Geraldine do?
She sold *doughnuts / ice cream*.

4 Who told Leandro it was a fun module?
Geraldine / Another student told him it was a fun module.

3 🔊 **21** **Listen again and choose T (true) or F (false).**

1 Geraldine sold *doughnuts* because they are her favourite food. T / F

2 You can run the business as part of your degree. T / F

3 You have to take a test about your business. T / F

4 Karen doesn't want to do the module. T / F

GRAMMAR

PAST SIMPLE QUESTIONS

1 Choose the correct question.

1. **a** What did you did?
   b What did you do?

2. **a** When did it start?
   b When did it started?

3. **a** What time did you get up today?
   b What time did you got up today?

4. **a** Where did you work in the summer?
   b Where did you worked in the summer?

5. **a** What did you bought?
   b What did you buy?

2 Write a short answer and a description.

1. Did she buy a suit? no (✗) /a skirt and a top (✓)
   No, she didn't. She bought a skirt and a top

2. Did he get the job? yes (✓) / take it (✗)
   _____

3. Did they volunteer? no (✗) / get a job (✓)
   _____

4. Did he apply for the job? yes (✓) / get an interview (✗)
   _____

5. Did he visit his parents? no (✗) / they come to visit him (✓)
   _____

3 Complete the questions with the words in the box.

| What   Where   Why   When   How |

1. _____ is his interview? Is it this afternoon?
2. _____ long did he work there?
3. _____ did you like about the job?
4. _____ was the company?
5. _____ didn't she take the job?

4 Write questions with *did* using the prompts.

1. where / your dad / work?
   Q: _Where did your dad work?_
   A: My dad worked for a mobile phone company.

2. how long / work there?
   Q: _____
   A: He worked there for 15 years.

3. like / his job?
   Q: _____
   A: Yes. He really liked his job.

4. why / he like it?
   Q: _____
   A: Because he liked the company and he liked the people in his team.

5. **Q:** where / work?
   A: He worked in an office in Manchester.

6. why / he leave?
   Q: _____
   A: He left when he was 65, because he wanted to stop working.

sandwich

A Sandwiches are a popular food in many cultures around the world. The word 'sandwich' comes from the Earl of Sandwich. He liked eating cold meat between two slices of bread, because he could continue working while he ate, but what is a sandwich degree?

B In 1998, in England, a government report stated that students benefited from more work experience. Companies also felt that students with experience were often better. Many universities started offering a degree with two years of study, one year in a company on work experience, and one final year studying. The work experience was the meat and the degree was the bread.

C These degrees became popular. Education changed a lot in the UK from the 1990s. In 1950, only 20 000 people went to university. In 1993, the numbers increased to about 100 000, and by 2010 over 300 000 people left with a degree. So work experience made you different.

D Many companies think that work experience is important. It makes students communicate better and work well in teams. Many students get jobs with the same company they did their work experience in.

READING

1 **(3 min)** **Read the text in three minutes and choose the best title.**

   a sandwiches and work
   b school and education
   c work experience

2 **Read the text again and match the paragraphs with the headings below.**

   1 a sandwich degree
   2 why these degrees became popular
   3 the history of the sandwich
   4 why experience is important

3 **Read the text again and choose T (true) or F (false).**

   1 The sandwich is a British food.   T / F
   2 Sandwich degrees last three years.   T / F
   3 Fewer people go to university in the UK today.   T / F
   4 Companies think team work is important.   T / F
   5 In the UK, fewer than 300 000 people left university with a degree in 2010.   T / F
   6 Companies often give jobs to students who did work experience with them.   T / F

4 **Match the words from the text to their definitions.**

   1 benefit (verb)
   2 degree (noun)
   3 popular (adj)
   4 government (noun)
   5 increase (verb)

   a liked and enjoyed by many people
   b the group of people who control a country
   c a qualification a student gets after studying a course at university
   d to make something larger in size or amount
   e to be helped by something

5 **Complete the sentences using the words in activity 4.**

   a Many people study to _____ their salary after university.
   b People vote for the _____ every four years.
   c A lot of people do Business Studies; it's a _____ degree.
   d More people get a _____ today than in the past.
   e Students today _____ from the internet because it's easier to find information.

GRAMMAR

PAST SIMPLE: IRREGULAR VERBS

1 Write the past simple form of the verbs.

1 do _____ 7 learn _____

2 feel _____ 8 make _____

3 find _____ 9 meet _____

4 get _____ 10 spend _____

5 give _____ 11 write _____

6 have _____

2 Rewrite the sentences in the negative form.

1 I went to work this morning.

2 I met my parents at the weekend.

3 I bought a new suit for the job.

4 I learned a lot of interesting things.

5 I got the job.

6 I found the office easily.

7 I had lunch with my manager.

8 I wrote a lot of emails.

9 I gave a 20-minute presentation.

10 I felt tired at the end of the day.

Living IELTS

TALKING ABOUT FEELINGS

Complete the sentences with the words in the box.

| nervous   confident   happy |

1 I am really _____ in my new job. It's the best job of my life!

2 I didn't feel _____ before my presentation, but I got lots of positive comments.

3 I'm quiet when I first meet people. I don't know what to say and I feel _____.

PRONUNCIATION

DIFFERENT PRONUNCIATIONS OF THE LETTER *e*

22 Listen to the pronunciation of the words. Circle the correct pronunciation of the sound in bold.

1	confid**e**nt	/iː/	/ə/	/e/
2	w**e**ll-paid	/iː/	/ə/	/e/
3	m**ee**t	/iː/	/ə/	/e/
4	r**ea**d	/iː/	/ə/	/e/
5	w**e**lcome	/iː/	/ə/	/e/
6	answ**er**	/iː/	/ə/	/e/

WRITING

LINKING SENTENCES WITH *SO*

1 **Match the two halves of the sentence.**

1. I speak three European languages, so
2. I worked in the summer holidays so
3. I lived in Spain for my gap year, so
4. I can't drive, so
5. I bought a new car so

a. that I had some money for this year.
b. they didn't offer me the job.
c. they asked me to work in the European headquarters.
d. that I can drive to work.
e. I learnt a lot more Spanish.

2 **Complete the text with the words in the box.**

> earn money   develop language skills
> get work experience

There are a lot of reasons to work when you are a student. I worked to ¹_____.
My course fees were very expensive. I also did it to ²_____ because companies want candidates with experience and education.
Many of my friends spent a year in another country, which is good to ³_____.
I am doing a French course now because the company I work for is French!

WRITING SKILLS

LINKING WITH *SO*

3 **Read the text again and complete the sentences to explain the reasons.**

1. I worked so _____
   _____.

2. I also worked so _____
   _____.

3. My friends went to another country so _____
   _____.

4 **Complete the text by adding *so* in <u>five</u> places.**

> My brother studies Business at a University in London. It is very expensive to live in London, he works as a waiter in an Italian restaurant at the weekends. He eats for free at the restaurant, he doesn't need to buy a lot of food.
>
> After his degree he wants to work for an international bank, he is also learning Spanish and German. My parents want him to get some work experience in a bank, they are not happy about his job in the restaurant. He knows my parents are right about this, he is now looking for new job in a bank.

TIME MANAGEMENT

University students are not only studying new courses, they are studying in a different educational setting. It's useful to learn how to cope with the differences between school and university.

1 **[◯ 23] Listen to Bruce, a student in Australia, talking about studying at university. Circle the three points he finds difficult.**

1 managing time and meeting deadlines
2 choosing where to study
3 having a choice of subjects
4 knowing the difference between free-time and independent study
5 taking responsibility for learning goals

2 **Read the statements and choose the best answer for you: Y (yes), N (no) or M (maybe).**

1 I often do other things (e.g. see my friends) rather than study.	Y / N / M
2 I know my weaknesses (e.g. chatting online).	Y / N / M
3 I do my homework just before the deadline.	Y / N / M
4 I forget to do my homework.	Y / N / M
5 I am late for classes.	Y / N / M
6 I forget or miss seminars.	Y / N / M
7 I miss deadlines.	Y / N / M
8 I know the time of day when I study best.	Y / N / M

3 **Read the text. Which tips do you use now? Which would you like to try?**

myBlog

There are lots of different ways you can improve your time management and manage your independent study. Here are my top five tips:

1 Find out where you are *wasting time – do you spend too much time surfing the net, reading emails or watching TV?

2 *Set priorities – write a list of everything you have to do and then put them in order of importance.

3 Start a routine – make a daily or weekly routine to organise your day or week.

4 Write a schedule for the week including all important events, e.g. seminars and deadlines.

5 Think about when you work best – is it easy to work in the morning or the evening? Do the difficult studying at your best time of the day.

Good luck! These tips worked for me. You can post your own tips below.

*waste time = to use time badly
*to set priorities = to decide on the order you do will things

4 **Read the chart and the information. Is it similar to your day? Then complete the chart below for your typical study day.**

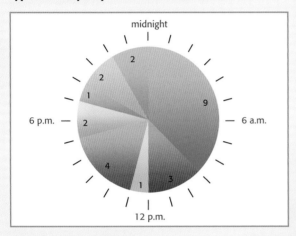

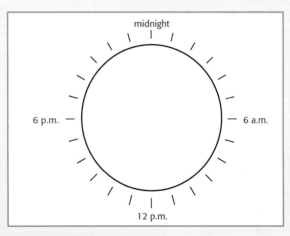

11 p.m.–8 a.m. sleep	2 p.m.–4 p.m. lessons
8 a.m.–9 a.m. breakfast	4 p.m.–5 p.m. independent study
9 a.m.–10 a.m. go to college	5 p.m.–6 p.m. gym
10 a.m.–12 a.m. lessons	6 p.m.–7 p.m. dinner
12 a.m.–1 p.m. independent study	7 p.m.–9 p.m. Facebook and emails
1 p.m.–2 p.m. lunch	9 p.m.–11 p.m. watch TV or a movie

My goals

Read your chart again and think about how you want to manage your time. Complete the table below.

How I manage my time now	How I want to manage my time
I'd like to practise speaking English more. I don't want to spend time chatting online.	Join a conversation class – one hour a day. Chat online every two days not every day.

Urban sports

READING

1 Read the text and choose the correct answers.

1 Tennis is popular in the UK …
 a in the spring
 b in autumn
 c all year round

2 In 'King of the Court' the ball can bounce …
 a three times
 b twice
 c once

3 To play the game you have to know how to play …
 a football and tennis
 b football and volleyball
 c tennis and volleyball

4 The game is played with … in each team.
 a two players
 b four players
 c six players

2 Complete the sentences with words from the text.

1 If you _____ two or more things you put them together.

2 To _____ is to put your hand or body on something.

3 _____ means on the other side from someone or something.

4 A _____ activity is something many people like.

5 To _____ is when a company pays to advertise their product at an event.

soccer tennis

In the game, players take opposite sides on a tennis court. They have to volley a football from side to side within the court. Players can't use their hands. They have to use their head, bodies and feet to return the ball. They can touch the ball three times before they have to hit it back. It can bounce once. Players try to land the ball somewhere so that their opponent can't return it. The serve is very important, so players have to serve well.

Anyone can play the game, but really good players usually know how to play tennis and volleyball. Each team has two players. The winning team has to get 15 points and it has to be two points in front of the other team. The service has to change every five points.

The game is very popular in the USA. There is a tournament series that is sponsored by companies. The question now is, when can we watch it on TV?

In England football is usually played in the autumn and tennis is usually played in the spring. In the USA, Anthony Maher is creating a sport that combines the two. King of the Court (or 'soccer tennis') is a sport that combines football, tennis and volleyball into one sport.

Grammar

Have to for obligation: can / can't for permission

1 Complete the rules for soccer tennis with *have to, don't have to, can* or *can't*.

1 You _____ have a football and a tennis court to play.
2 You _____ be a professional, but it _____ help to know how to play volleyball and tennis.
3 You _____ use your hands.
4 You _____ use your feet, body and head.
5 Each team _____ only touch the ball three times before they _____ hit it back.
6 The ball _____ only bounce once.
7 The winning team _____ get to 15 points and _____ be two points in front of the other team.
8 You _____ change service after five points.

2 Look at the pictures and complete the sentences with *can* or *can't*.

1 You _____ fish here.

2 You _____ drive faster than 50 miles per hour here.

3 You _____ park here.

4 You _____ swim here.

5 You _____ see this film if you are 15 or over.

6 You _____ smoke here.

3 Complete the sentences using *have to* and *don't have to*.

1 You _don't have to_ (✗) be 18 to drive in England – you can drive at 17, but you _have to_ (✓) drive on the left.
2 You _____ (✓) use your feet to play football, but you _____ (✓) use your hands for a throw in.
3 You _____ (✗) young to play sports, but you _____ (✓) be fit.
4 You _____ (✗) fly from London to Paris, but you _____ (✓) have a passport to travel.

Pronunciation

Strong and weak forms: *have to*

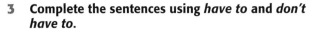

24 Listen to the sentences. Circle the correct answers.

1 I have to go now! *strong / weak*
2 I don't have to, but I want to read this essay tonight. *strong / weak*
3 Yes, you have to do your homework. *strong / weak*
4 I collected the books so you don't have to. *strong / weak*

Vocabulary

Sports and sports skills

1 Complete the sentences with the words in the box.

> balance   bounce   climb   hit   jump   kick

1 In basketball, players _____ the ball using their hands.

2 _____ is very important in gymnastics.

3 The ball can go forward in rugby when you _____ it.

4 There are two events that test the ability to _____: the high jump and the long jump.

5 You use a racket in tennis to _____ the ball back.

6 You need safety equipment to _____ a mountain.

2 Match the photos with the sports in activity 1.

3 Complete the crossword about sports.

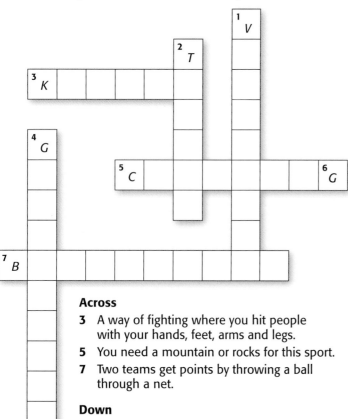

Across

3 A way of fighting where you hit people with your hands, feet, arms and legs.

5 You need a mountain or rocks for this sport.

7 Two teams get points by throwing a ball through a net.

Down

1 You use your hands and arms to hit the ball over a high net.

2 You can play singles or doubles. You have to hit a ball over a net with a racket.

4 Activities that test your strength and skill.

6 You use a club to hit a small ball into a very small hole.

4 Complete the notes below.

Sports I watch: _____

Sports I play: _____

Sports I think are boring: _____

Sports I don't like: _____

Sports I think are dangerous: _____

GRAMMAR

NEED

1 Match the pictures to the sports below.

1	Volleyball	4	Football
2	Judo	5	Climbing
3	Tennis	6	Ping Pong

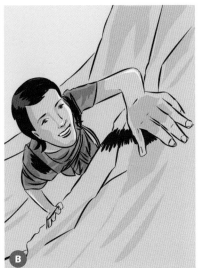

2 Match the descriptions to the sports in activity 1.

a You don't need a ball or a bat. You just need an opponent.

b You need a net but you don't need a racket.

c You need rackets, balls and a court.

d You need 22 players, a ball and a pitch.

e You need balls and a bat but you don't need a court. You do need a table though.

f You just need yourself and a mountain.

3 Complete the sentences with _need_ or _don't need_.

1 You _____ a racket, a ball and a court to play tennis.

2 You _____ to be fit to play some sports, like pool or darts.

3 You _____ to practise a lot at any sport to become good.

4 You _____ to be young to be good at sports, but it helps.

5 You _____ lots of sports equipment to keep fit.

6 You _____ a bike to take part in a triathlon.

4 Put the lines of this conversation in the correct order.

a You need to wear good quality sports shoes and you need shorts and a T-shirt. ____

b Well, first you need to buy a tennis racket and some tennis balls. Then you need some clothes to wear. ____

c What kind of clothes do I need? ____

d Yes. You need a hat if you play in sunny weather. ____

e I want to start tennis lessons. What do I need to buy? ____

f Anything else? Do I need a hat? ____

5 Correct the mistakes in the sentences.

1 You don't need be tall to do the long jump.

2 Do you needs to be very fit to play ping pong?

3 You needing 11 people to make a football team.

4 You not need a racket to do judo.

5 Need you a new tennis racket?

LISTENING

1 ⊙ 25 **Listen to Tom and Alice talking about keeping fit. Choose the correct answers.**

1 Alice … what kangoo jumps are.
   a knows   **b** doesn't know

2 They are … for your bones.
   a good   **b** bad

3 These shoes make exercise more …
   a dangerous   **b** fun

4 Alice … jogging.
   a loves   **b** hates

5 They can help you get … faster
   a fitter   **b** stronger

6 Alice … to try them.
   a doesn't want   **b** wants

SPORTS QUIZ!

3 **How much do you know about sports? Circle the correct answer.**

1 How many players are on a volleyball team?
   a 6   **b** 11   **c** 5

2 Where is the Nad Al-Sheba racecourse?
   a Abu-Dhabi   **b** Jeddah   **c** Dubai

3 Which of these sports is <u>not</u> popular world-wide?
   a football   **b** baseball   **c** tennis

4 In which country is ice-hockey really popular?
   a Canada   **b** India   **c** South Africa

5 At the 2008 Olympics, which country won all the medals in table tennis?
   a Thailand   **b** Japan   **c** China

6 In tennis, what does *deuce* mean?
   a when a player serves the ball
   b a score of 15/15
   c a score of 40/40

7 What does *LBW* mean in cricket?
   a leg before wicket
   b long ball wide
   c late ball win

8 Which team does <u>not</u> play in the Rubgy Six Nations tournament?
   a Italy   **b** Germany   **c** Scotland

2 ⊙ 25 **Listen again. Choose Y (yes) or N (no).**

1 Can you do exercise classes in them?   Y / N
2 Do you have to use these shoes for running?   Y / N
3 Does Tom like running?   Y / N
4 Does Tom think they are dangerous?   Y / N

Living IELTS

ADDING EMPHASIS (1)

Complete the sentences with the words in the box.

| really   even   so   such   absolutely |

1 There are _____ a lot of different sports to try!
2 It's _____ fantastic!
3 You can _____ play it on your computer.
4 You can watch it in _____ many places.
5 It's _____ difficult.

WRITING

DISCUSSING A CHART

1   Read the pie chart and answer the questions.

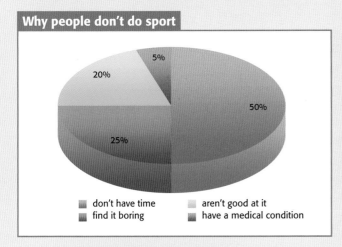

Why people don't do sport

- ■ don't have time
- ■ find it boring
- ■ aren't good at it
- ■ have a medical condition

1   What does the pie chart show?
2   What reasons do people give?
3   What is the most common reason?
4   What is the least common reason?

2   Complete the description using the words and phrases in the box.

> one in five   smallest   fifty per cent
> shows   key   twenty-five

The pie chart ¹ _____ why people don't do sport. In the ² _____ at the bottom of the chart, we can see the percentage of people and the reasons. ³ _____ of people don't do sport because they don't have time. ⁴ _____ per cent, or a quarter of people, don't do sport because they find it boring. ⁵ _____ people don't do sport because they aren't good at it. Finally, five per cent, the ⁶ _____ group, don't do sport because of a medical condition.

WRITING SKILLS

LINKING WITH *BECAUSE*

3   Read the pie chart. Complete the sentences with a reason.

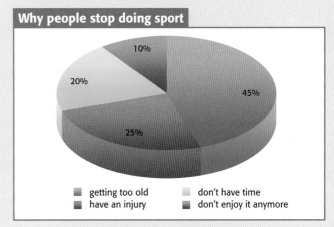

Why people stop doing sport

- ■ getting too old
- ■ have an injury
- ■ don't have time
- ■ don't enjoy it anymore

1   45% of people stop doing sport because ...
2   25% stop doing sport because ...
3   20% of people stop because ...
4   One in ten people stop because ...

4   Write a paragraph describing the pie chart in activity 3. Use the model in activity 2 to help you.

The pie chart shows _____

_____

_____

_____

_____

_____

_____

_____

_____

_____

IMPROVING YOUR VOCABULARY 2

Good language learners try different techniques to help them learn words and improve their vocabulary. There are many different techniques and you should choose the ones that work best for you.

1 Look at the statements below. Tick the techniques that are true for you.

1 I like seeing words written down. I can't remember a word from just hearing it.

2 I learn words best by listening and repeating them.

3 I like to learn words by translating.

4 I write the word in lots of different sentences to remember it.

5 I like learning words in groups. For example, by topic or function.

6 I like walking around the room while I learn words.

2 26 Listen to Andre and Carole describing how they learn vocabulary. Tick the methods they use.

		Andre	Carole
1	putting words into groups		
2	making a link to a picture		
3	saying words aloud		
4	using words in sentences		

Now you're going to try two of these techniques.

3 Putting words into groups can help you remember more words. How many groups can you make from the words in the box below? Can you add other words to the groups?

> Biology   climb   flat   awful   Sociology   amazing   hit   house   interesting
> bedsit   jump   boring   Law   kick   Engineering   student hall

4 Making a link to a picture can help some learners. Look back at the sports vocabulary on pages 54–55 and try this technique.

1 Think of a picture for each word or try to remember where you were when you first learned the word.

2 Write the word on a piece of card and put the cards in a bag.

3 Pull out a card and try to think of the picture or the place. Can you remember the meaning?

My goals

Try a technique from activity 2 this week. Tell a classmate the technique you're going to use. At the end of the week:

1 Tell your classmate what you liked and didn't like about the technique.

2 Ask your classmate to test you on the new words.

3 Continue with this technique or try another one – find a technique that works for you.

SPEAKING PART 2

In Part 2 of the Speaking test, the examiner gives you a topic to speak about. You have one minute to prepare what you're going to say and to make notes. Then you talk about the topic for one to two minutes.

1 Read the Part 2 task card and answer the questions.

1 What's the main topic? _____
2 How many main points are there? _____
3 What's the final point? _____

> **Describe an important historical building you like. You should say:**
> - where it is
> - what it looks like
> - why it is important
> And why you like the building.

2 Match the notes below with the points on the task card.

1 It is one of the Queen of England's palaces. It's nearly 200 years old and it is her main home.

2 Buckingham Palace is in London.

3 It's a big grey building with gates around the outside. It's not very high but it's large. There are nearly 800 rooms and over 200 bedrooms.

4 I enjoyed going on a tour there.

3 🔘 **27** Listen to two students answering Part 2. Tick the mistakes they make.

4 ⏱(1min) Read the task card in activity 1 again and make notes on each point in one minute.

5 ⏱(2min) Give your answer. Speak aloud for one to two minutes. Use your notes from activity 4 to help you organise your answer.

Exam Tip 👆

Complete the tips below using words from the box.

> organise   prepare   notes

1 Use the one minute to _____ well.
2 Make _____ on all the points on the task card.
3 Use the task card and your notes to _____ your answer.

	Chen Chen	Juan
doesn't give a long answer		
doesn't include all the points		
doesn't follow the order of the points		

Unit 8

The natural world

VOCABULARY

LANDSCAPE FEATURES

1 **Complete the sentences with the words in the box.**

> cliffs   coast   rainforest   beach
> river   ocean   waves   waterfall

1 The Amazon _____ is the biggest in the world and the second longest _____ in the world goes through the middle.

2 Forty-eight countries in the world do not have a _____. These include Afghanistan, Austria, Mali, Nepal and Paraguay.

3 Bangladesh's Cox's Bazar is the world's longest sandy _____ at 150km.

4 The _____ in England are white.

5 The Pacific _____ is the deepest in the world.

6 The Hawaiian islands have some of the biggest _____ in the world.

7 Venezuela has the highest _____ in the world.

2 **Complete the text with the words in the box.**

> scenery   destination   landscape
> spectacular   unique

Indonesia is a ^{1} _____ place because it has the world's largest population of people living on a group of islands. It has some of the best natural ^{2} _____ in the world. Java is the most populated island in the world, but it has a ^{3} _____ with volcanoes and rainforests. There are 50 national parks in Indonesia. There are six ^{4} _____ parks which are World Heritage listed. This beautiful country is the ^{5} _____ of nearly seven million tourists every year.

Listening

1 🔘 28 **Listen to two friends talking about California. Choose Y (yes) or N (no).**

1	Has he made holiday plans?	Y / N
2	Has he been to America before?	Y / N
3	Has he read much about California?	Y / N
4	Has he been on a driving holiday before?	Y / N
5	Has he booked the hotels?	Y / N
6	Has he tried skiing before?	Y / N

2 🔘 28 **Listen again. When did Halide do each of these things? Complete the sentences.**

1 She went to New York

_____.

2 She went to California

_____.

3 She went on a driving holiday

_____.

4 She went skiing _____.

Vocabulary

Adjective and noun collocations

1 **Look at the photos and complete the collocations.**

1 sandy b_____
2 deep r_____
3 spectacular v_____
4 snowy m_____
5 thick rainf_____
6 extinct v_____

2 **Complete the text using the collocations from activity 1.**

When people think of California they imagine lots of ¹ _____ on the coast and lots of sunny weather. But California has a lot more. The ² _____ are excellent for people who want to ski. They also offer ³ _____ across the Sierra Nevada and other mountain features such as numerous ⁴ _____, but some might be active! San Francisco is famous for the Golden Gate Bridge which stands over the ⁵ _____. On the north coast there are the ⁶ _____ that cover over 540km².

Living IELTS

Commenting

1 🔘 29 **Listen and complete the conversation.**

A: I'm going to Hawaii next week.
B: Hawaii!? ¹ _____!
That sounds ² _____!
A: Yeah! And I'm going surfing.
B: ³ _____! That sounds ⁴ _____!
A: Yeah, I can't wait!

2 🔘 29 **Complete the conversation. Then listen and check.**

A: I'm going to Jeddah next week.
B: Jeddah!? ¹ _____!
That sounds ² _____!
A: Yeah! And I'm going scuba diving.
B: ³ _____!
That sounds ⁴ _____!
A: Yeah, I can't wait!

Grammar

Present perfect simple + *ever* and *never*; past simple

1 Complete the sentences with the correct form of the verbs.

1 I _____ (go) to China, but people say it is amazing.
2 I _____ (travel) to Dubai many times. It's great for winter sun.
3 You _____ (finish) your homework, so you can't go out.
4 We _____ (fly). We always drive or take the ferry.
5 He _____ (visit) the Himalayas a few years ago.

2 Correct the mistakes in <u>three</u> of the questions.

1 Did you ever go to Vietnam?
2 Did she enjoy her holiday?
3 Have she ever been surfing?
4 Have you ever played golf?
5 Has she ever been to New York?
6 Did she ever eat sushi?

3 Complete the questions with the correct form of the verbs.

> be x2   play x2   meet x2

1 _____ you _____ John before?
2 _____ you _____ your parents last week?
3 _____ you _____ to Australia?
4 _____ you at the festival? I was there on Sunday.
5 _____ you _____ football yesterday?
6 _____ you _____ golf before?

READING

1 Read the text and match the headings with the paragraphs.

1 The people of Madagascar
2 What makes Madagascar special?
3 Environmental damage in Madagascar
4 Where is Madagascar?

2 Read the text again. Choose T (true) or F (false).

1 Lots of people go on holiday to Madagascar. T / F
2 Madagascar is a rich country. T / F
3 Many plants and animals are unique to Madagascar. T / F
4 Madagascar's population is causing problems for the island. T / F
5 The forest damage is worst on the coast. T / F
6 Some species of lemur are in danger. T / F

**Sambava
Masoala National Park**

Antananarivo

**Isalo
National Park**

The changing environment of Madagascar

A Madagascar is the fourth largest island in the world. It is located in the Indian Ocean off the southeastern coast of Africa. The country is quite poor and most people earn less than $2 a day. However, there is growing interest in the country for tourism, but at the moment very few tourists visit.

B Madagascar has something special which makes it very interesting for scientists and tourists alike. It has many species of plants and animals that do not exist in other countries. Between 80 and 90 percent of its animals and plants have only ever been found in Madagascar.

C People have lived in Madagascar for a very long time. Most researchers believe that the first people came to the island over 2000 years ago from Borneo in the South China Sea.

However, since then Arabs and East Africans, and later Malays, Javanese, Indians, Chinese and Europeans have all lived in Madagascar. The population has risen to over 20 million people and this has caused many environmental problems.

D Nearly fifty percent of Madagascar's forests have disappeared in the last fifty years. It is even higher on the coast. Scientists have estimated that nearly 50 per cent of Madagascar's animal and plant species are dead or will die. Madgascar's most famous animal is the lemur. Unfortunately, at least 17 species of lemur have become extinct since people arrived. Many plants and animals we know little about will be dead before we have a chance to know more about them.

GRAMMAR

PRESENT PERFECT WITH *FOR* AND *SINCE*

1 **Match the sentences with the grammar explanations below.**

1 I have lived here *for* three years.
2 *How long* have you lived here?
3 I have been in England *since* August.

a The start of the action.
b To talk about the time period of the action.
c To ask about the period of time or start of the action.

2 **Complete the sentences with *for*, *since* or *how long*.**

1 I haven't been to Italy _____ a long time.
2 _____ have you worked here?
3 We haven't eaten here _____ your birthday.
4 _____ have you known her?
5 I have known about the essay _____ the start of term.
6 I've had an iPhone _____ ages.

3 **Correct the mistakes in <u>three</u> of the sentences.**

1 We've been in Japan since a month.
2 I've lived here since I was five.
3 She's loved surfing since many years.
4 I have skied every winter for the last five years.
5 They've worked here for 2010.

PRONUNCIATION

STRONG AND WEAK FORMS: *HAVE* AND *HAS*

1 **30 Listen to the sentences and underline the stressed (strong) sounds.**

1 Have you ever been to Madagascar?
2 Yes, I have.
3 Has he ever seen a lemur?
4 No, he hasn't.

2 **30 Listen again and repeat the sentences.**

GAP YEAR

A Many students in the UK take a gap year after school and before going to university. In fact about 250 000 do every year. Most of them want to combine travel with making money or doing *voluntary work. But whatever their reasons, students need to think carefully about what they do. There are a number of advantages to taking a gap year.

B First of all, it gives people time to decide what degree they want to do and what job they want to have in the future. It also allows them to learn more about the world, for example, learning different languages, experiencing different cultures and seeing landscapes they have never seen before.

C However, many people argue that travelling for a year is just a long holiday. It is also expensive and it might be better to spend the money on education. Some students also forget how to study during their gap year and find it hard to study again when they return home.

D In conclusion, there are a lot of advantages and disadvantages in taking a gap year. In my opinion, a gap year is a valuable experience, but one whole year is too long.

*Voluntary work is work that you do because you want to, not because you have to do it. Volunteers work to make things better and are not paid for what they do.

WRITING

THE ADVANTAGES AND DISADVANTAGES OF A GAP YEAR

1 Read the text and answer the questions.

   a What is a gap year?
   b What are the advantages of a gap year?
   c What are the disadvantages of a gap year?

2 Read the text again and match the functions 1–4 with the paragraphs A–D.

   1 giving the writer's opinion
   2 listing the bad things about a gap year
   3 introducing the topic
   4 listing the good things about a gap year

WRITING SKILLS

PRESENTING AN ARGUMENT

3 Read the text again and answer the questions.

> In my opinion   However   For example   First of all

   1 Which word introduces the opposite idea?
   2 Which phrase shows what the writer thinks?
   3 Which phrase helps lists one of many points?
   4 Which phrase introduces an explanation?

4 Complete the paragraph below with words and phrases from activity 3.

> There are some benefits to spending a year travelling. ¹ _____, you can visit more places than in a one or two week holiday. ² _____, you cannot spend time in the Amazon rainforest, climb the snowy Himalayas and relax on the sandy Australian beaches in one week. ³ _____, people who have spent a long time travelling feel bored. They don't enjoy travelling by plane, boat, train and bus anymore. ⁴ _____, people who can travel for a year are very lucky but they need to plan carefully.

5 Read the essay title and write a paragraph about it. Use the model in activity 4 to help you. Use *First of all*, *For example*, *However* and *In my opinion*.

> Gap years are an important experience. Do you agree or disagree?

CHECKING YOUR WORK

All students make mistakes when learning new language. It is a normal part of learning. It is important to read or listen to teacher comments and check your work for any common mistakes you make.

1 Match the teacher comments with the sentences below.

1 'Check your grammar. Is the tense correct?'
2 'Check your spelling carefully.'
3 'Check the verb form matches the subject.'
4 'This is a formal essay and your vocabulary is too informal.'
5 'Check your word formation. You need a verb not a noun.'
6 'Check you use the correct plural form of the noun.'

A There are many international student in the UK.

B I go to the shopping mall yesterday.

C He work for a large IT company.

D It is difficult to communication in another language.

E You need to reffer to the chart.

F Many kids fail in school because they are tested too much.

2 Correct the sentences in activity 1.

3 Read the paragraph and correct the underlined mistakes. Use the teacher comments in activity 1 to help you.

Many student in the UK take a gap year after school. They wants to see other countries before go to university. They can saw the world and experiencing a new culture. For many it is the best year of their life. It don't have to be a long holiday – many people work. There is the arguement that people should work to pay for univercity.

4 🔘 31 **Listen to Luca talking to his teacher. Circle the three things he needs to improve.**

1 organisation   2 grammar   3 vocabulary   4 spelling

My goals

Read any teacher comments you have and complete the table below.

The most common mistakes I make	How I plan to improve
Poor paragraph structure	Re-write my paragraphs and ask my teacher to look at it again.

LISTENING FOR SPECIFIC INFORMATION

In the Listening test, you need to listen for specific information in a conversation. For example, names, numbers or places.

1 🔊 **32** Listen and circle the number you hear.

1	15	50	**5**	£35	£53
2	116	160	**6**	777289	772289
3	3:20	2:40	**7**	58 kilos	85 kilos
4	7th	7	**8**	07789 471147	07889 471147

2 Read the text below and predict which answers could include numbers. Then predict which column could contain answers following *What* and *Where* questions.

Programme of activities for first day		
Time	**Place**	**Event**
9.00	¹ _____	Register
9.30	Main hall	² _____
³ _____	Library	⁴ _____

3 🔊 **33** Listen and complete the table.

4 Labelling diagrams is another type of task that asks you to listen for specific information. Read the diagram below. How many rooms do you have to label?

Library (L)   Staff Room (SR)   Toilet (T)
Main Hall (MH)   Classroom (CR)

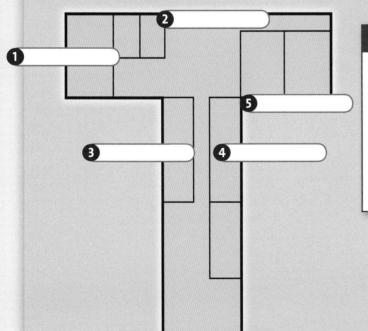

5 Choose T (true) or F (false).

1 The main hall is next to the canteen.   T / F
2 Go past a classroom to get to the staff room.   T / F
3 The reception is opposite the canteen.   T / F
4 The main hall is at the end of the corridor.   T / F

6 🔊 **33** Listen again and complete the diagram.

Exam Tip 👆

Complete the tips using the words in the box.

read   predict   revise

1 Read the instructions and try to _____ the information you will hear.
2 _____ the sounds of numbers.
3 _____ the text or the diagrams carefully.

VOCABULARY

MY FAMILY

1 **Complete these sentences with a word or phrase from the box below.**

> the middle child   big   the oldest child
> come from   the youngest child   an only child

1 I come from a _____
   family. I have four brothers and three sisters.

2 I _____ a small family. I only have one
   sister.

3 I'm _____. I don't have
   any brothers or sisters.

4 I'm _____ and it's difficult!
   My brothers and sisters never listen to me!

5 I'm _____. Klara is older
   than me and Richard is younger than me.

6 I'm 20 and I'm _____.
   Tala is 18 and Ahmed is 16.

READING

1 **Look at the photo. Decide if these statements are T (true) or F (false).**

1	The child on the left is an only child.	T / F
2	The children are brothers and sisters.	T / F
3	The oldest child is in the middle.	T / F
4	The youngest child is on the right.	T / F
5	The middle child is on the left.	T / F

2 **Read the text and match the headings with the paragraphs.**

1 The unlucky child.
2 The importance of birth order.
3 Why does this happen?
4 A future film star?
5 The best position.

A _____

Do you have brothers or sisters or are you an only child? Are you the oldest, the youngest or somewhere in the middle? These are important questions because the position influences your personality and your future success.

B _____

Middle children are often good at making everyone happy. Unfortunately they are not usually rich. Often they are not well-educated and don't have a good job. They get less attention than older children, and less money and time are spent on them. Don't worry about being a middle child though – famous and successful middle children include Bill Gates, JFK and Madonna.

3 **Read the text again. Choose T (true) or F (false).**

1 Middle children are unlikely to have a lot of money. T / F
2 Middle children are not good with other people. T / F
3 Middle children are never successful. T / F
4 Older siblings play a lot with the youngest child. T / F
5 The youngest children are often very creative. T / F
6 Not many US presidents are oldest children. T / F
7 Oldest children don't want to be successful. T / F
8 Money and attention are important for a child's future success. T / F
9 Big families can be bad for a child's development in poor families. T / F

4 **Read the comments and match them with the correct photograph, A, B or C.**

1 Me? I'm a relaxed sort of person. I don't know what I want to be when I'm older. I don't want to be a banker or anything – I'm not interested in money. I like people; I like making them feel good, so I want to work in a team.

2 What do I like? I like playing. I like making things. Last week I made a car out of old boxes and paper. I painted it yellow, red and blue! When I'm older I want to be a painter.

3 What am I interested in? A lot of things. I work hard and I think I'm intelligent too. I like taking care of my younger brothers and sisters – they're good kids! And when I'm older? I know what I want to be. I want to be a doctor!

A **A YOUNGEST CHILD**

B **A MIDDLE CHILD**

C **AN OLDEST CHILD**

C _____

The youngest children are often very creative. They are given lots of attention from their older brothers and sisters. So their games and entertainment are often more creative. Many youngest children have successful careers in journalism, sales and the arts. Lots of famous actors and actresses are youngest children.

D _____

The most successful children are only children and first born children. More than half of all Nobel Prize winners and U.S. presidents are first born children. Also more people studying medicine, law and engineering are first born than middle or youngest. While middle children are easy-going, first borns are ambitious and aggressive. They are also often more intelligent and have a higher *IQ than their *siblings.

E _____

So how can we explain these differences? Well, first born and only children have more attention. With regards to only children – there is more money in a small family, so more money is spent on them. The diet of children can also be different because more money is spent on food in smaller families. First borns and only children are spoken to more like an adults and spend more time with adults. As a result, if the family has another child, the oldest becomes like another parent.

*Siblings is a formal word for brothers and sisters. I have three siblings.
*IQ (Intelligence Quotient) is a number based on a test that represents a person's intelligence. She's intelligent; she has an IQ of 115.

GRAMMAR

PRESENT SIMPLE PASSIVE

1 **Write the present simple forms of the verbs below.**

1 celebrated   _____
2 given   _____
3 made   _____
4 saved   _____
5 spent   _____
6 spoken   _____

2 **Complete the sentences with the correct form of the verbs.**

1 Middle children _____ (give) less attention.
2 Oldest children _____ (speak) to more by their parents.
3 The birth of all children _____ (celebrate) but often the first child is the most celebrated.
4 Youngest children _____ (make) to feel important by older brothers and sisters.
5 Less money _____ (spend) on younger children's education.
6 More money _____ (save) for the oldest child's future.

3 **Match the two halves of the sentences.**

1 Oldest children are encouraged to be more ambitious
2 Youngest children are given more attention
3 It is not all bad for middle children. Success is achieved
4 The differences are made smaller

a by some people.
b by their parents.
c by their brothers and sisters.
d by having lots of money.

4 **Complete the text with the correct form of the verbs.**

Mother's Day and Father's Day are special events in many countries and [1] _____ (celebrate) with a lunch or a party. These are traditional days when friends and relatives [2] _____ (invite). Now countries have introduced other 'special' days. In America, the first Sunday after Labour Day [3] _____ (call) Grandparents Day. The 20th of November [4] _____ (know) as Children's Day. Both these days [5] _____ (celebrate) as much as Mother's and Father's Day now and presents [6] _____ (give).

Vocabulary

Family relationships

1 Label the people in Paola's family tree with the words in the box.

> father   grandmother   brother-in-law
> mother   sister-in-law   grandfather

Grandparents

Claudia   Alfredo

Parents

Lucia   Roberto

Claudio   Cynthia
Salvatore   *sister*

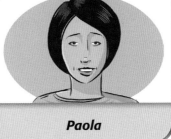

Paola

Brother

Luca   Donatella
Antonia

2 Complete the sentences with the words in the box.

> aunt   uncle   son   daughter
> niece   nephew   cousin

1 Salvatore is Antonia's _____.
2 Paola hasn't got any _____ or _____.
   Her parents are both only children.
3 Salvatore is the _____ of Claudio and Cynthia.
4 Antonia is the _____ of Luca and Donatella.
5 Antonia is Paola's _____.
6 Salvatore is Paola's _____.

Grammar

Passive and active verbs

1 Rewrite the sentences using the active form.

1 Different food is eaten in Kodinhi.
They _____

2 Different drinks are drunk in Kodinhi.
They _____

3 It is not believed to be genetic.
Doctors _____

4 More research needs to be done.
Scientists _____

2 Complete the text using the passive or active form of the verbs.

Blue Zone

A 'Blue Zone' is a place on Earth where many people [1] _____ (have) a healthy lifestyle and often live to 100. The Five Blue Zones [2] _____ (locate) in – the Italian island of Sardinia; Okinawa, Japan; Loma Linda, California; Costa Rica's isolated Nicoya Peninsula, and Ikaria, an isolated Greek island. These places [3] _____ (spread) across the whole world, so what do they have in common? In all these places a healthy diet [4] _____ (eat). People who live in these places [5] _____ (eat) only a small amount of sugar, meat and fat. Exercise [6] _____ (take) everyday, but not in a gym. People [7] _____ (use) their bodies just to do their jobs. Also people in the Blue Zones [8] _____ (live) a less stressful life and have a close family.

Listening

1 🔊 34 **Listen to a lecture on twins. Put the topics in order.**

a An unusual Indian village.
b Why is this happening?
c Twins are not very common.
d Who normally has twins?
e How many twins are there?

2 🔊 34 **Listen again. Choose T (true) or F (false).**

1 We all know lots of twins. T / F
2 There are 2000 sets of twins in Kodinhi. T / F
3 We don't know how many twins there are. T / F
4 Dr Sribiju thinks the food may cause lots of twins. T / F
5 Lots of twins are born in Asia. T / F
6 More twins are born to smaller women. T / F

3 Put the words in order to make questions.

1 located / it / is / Where ?
2 it / special / is / Why ?
3 normally / How many / are / born / twins / in Asia?
4 has / normally / Who / twins ?

4 Answer the questions in activity 3 for you.

Living IELTS

Adding emphasis (2)

Choose the correct answers.

1 Opinions about birth order is *far / really* from accurate but it is interesting.
2 I *do / far* believe birth order influences your success.
3 I *really / far* feel my parents bought more things for my brother.
4 I *do / far* think the idea of birth order is stupid.
5 What I *like most / Truly* is spending time with my family.
6 Parents *truly / do* treat younger children differently.

WRITING

DESCRIBING A TABLE

1 Read the table and answer the questions.

  a What does the table show?
  b What years does it compare?
  c Is the cost increasing or decreasing?
  d What are the three most expensive things?

The cost of raising a child		
Expenditure	**2009 costs**	**2003 costs**
Childcare	£54696	£32853
Education	£52881	£32593
Food	£17490	£14918
Clothing	£14035	£11360
Holidays	£13207	£11458
Babysitting	£11003	£6760
Hobbies & Toys	£10780	£8861
Leisure	£7772	£6366
Pocket money	£4338	£3386
Furniture	£2770	£2074
Personal	£1107	£925
Other	£11731	£8845
Total	£201809	£140398

copyright © LV = Life and Pensions

WRITING SKILLS

COMPARING FIGURES IN A TABLE

2 Complete the description of the table with the words in the box.

> childcare   total   over   clothing   food

This table shows how much money parents spend on their children. The [1] _____ cost of raising a child in the UK is now over £200000. The most money is spent on [2] _____. It costs [3] _____ £50000. This is nearly three times the cost of [4] _____. Holidays and [5] _____ cost almost the same.

3 Read the table and write sentences using the prompts and the words in the box.

> almost the same   more   the most
> twice the cost   the least

  1 personal expenses
  2 holidays / babysitting
  3 childcare
  4 hobbies and toys / babysitting
  5 clothing / leisure and recreation

4 Write a paragraph describing the table. Use the model in activity 2 and the sentences you wrote in activity 3 to help you.

USING A DICTIONARY

Good language learners always use a dictionary and some learners use more than one dictionary. A learner's dictionary is for international students and it can be a very useful reference for you studying.

1 Tick the dictionaries you own and use. Which one is your favourite? Why?

monolingual ☐ learner's ☐ mobile app ☐
English-English ☐ bilingual ☐ online ☐

2 Read the dictionary entry and label the parts in the box below.

sound file   *phonetic script   most common use   definition   part of speech   example sentence

3 ⟶ **4** ⟶ **2** ⟶

celebration / selɪˈbreɪʃən / *noun* [C, U] celebration 🔊 **5** **6**

1

1 N-COUNTABLE the act of doing something enjoyable because it is a special day to remember. *The celebration of my twenty-first birthday begins at 8 p.m. with a big dinner.*

2 N-UNCOUNTABLE an occasion when something good happens. *Getting a good score on your IELTS is cause for celebration.*

*phonetic script: symbols which show the pronunciation of words

3 All dictionaries are different. Put a tick in the table for the dictionary entry in activity 2 and your favourite dictionary. Does your favourite dictionary have all the features?

features	dictionary entry in activity 2	your favourite dictionary
definition		
most common use		
example sentence		
sound file		
phonetic script		
part of speech		

4 Go to your favourite online dictionary. (If you don't have one, try searching for one in your web browser.) What features does it have? Try typing in new vocabulary from Unit 9 and learning about the different features.

My goals

Think about how you use a dictionary at the moment and how you can learn more with your dictionary in the future. Complete the table with your goals.

Now I use a dictionary too...	In the future I'm going to use a dictionary too...
Look up the meaning of the word	Learn collocations of important words

READING STRATEGY 2

In the Reading test, you answer different types of questions. It's important to understand what the different types of questions are and what you need to do for each one.

1 Match the question types to the instructions below.

1 yes / no / not given questions
2 short answer questions
3 matching headings and paragraphs
4 multiple choice questions

A Who is more creative? _____

B why birth order is important   Paragraph A

C Birth order is important in success.   Y / N / NG

d ... children are more successful.
(a) Older   (b) Younger

2 ○35 Listen to two students discussing the different question types. Number the question types in the order they are mentioned.

1 yes/no/not given questions ☐
2 short answer questions ☐
3 matching headings and paragraphs ☐
4 multiple choice questions ☐

3 ○35 Listen again and complete the sentences.

1 Read the _____ of each paragraph carefully because it has the main idea.
2 You should look for the answers in the same _____ as the text.
3 Short answer questions usually test _____, so make sure you know what you're looking for.
4 When you can't find an answer it probably means it is _____.

4 Read the text and answer the questions below. Use the advice in activity 3 to help you.

The population of the planet is 7 billion and it is forecast to reach 9 billion by 2050. Many people believe there are too many of us on the planet and there are not enough resources (e.g. energy, food, water, etc.).

In different countries around the world, people use resources at different rates. The average American and European person uses more energy, food and water than people in other parts of the world. Scientists say we need the resources of four planets for everyone in the world to live like people in America and Europe.

The problem is that now many developing countries want to have lifestyles like Americans and Europeans. Countries like China and India have a population of over 1 billion people each. These countries have strong economies and they are using more and more resources.

1 The size of the population is not a problem.   Y / N / NG
2 Many countries do not have enough electricity.   Y / N / NG
3 India and China could cause problems in the future.   Y / N / NG

5 Choose a reading text in the Student's Book and try using the advice in activity 3 again.

Exam Tip

Complete the tips using the words in the box.

spend   text   understand   multiple

1 Always answer a question with _____ options.
2 When you can't find the answer for _____ Y / N / NG, choose NG.
3 Don't _____ too much time on one question because you won't have time to finish the test.
4 You do not need to _____ everything about the topic.

Unit 10

Conservation

READING

1 **Read the text about the Aral Sea. What is the significance of these numbers?**

1 7 billion
2 400
3 1960
4 1963 and 1998

2 **Which paragraph is mostly about…**

1 the Aral Sea?
2 the amount of water we use?
3 the problems caused?
4 Lake Chad?

3 **Read the text again. Choose T (true) or F (false).**

1 The average person uses 400 gallons of water per day.   T / F
2 More than 240 billion bottles of water are sold every year.   T / F
3 The Aral Sea is in Russia.   T / F
4 The Aral Sea got smaller because of farming.   T / F
5 Lots of people lost their jobs as the Aral Sea got smaller.   T / F
6 Lake Chad is 95% smaller than it was in 1963.   T / F

4 **Find the words in the text and choose the correct definition.**

1 demands
   a the amount of something people want
   b to say very strongly that you want something

2 border
   a the location of a river
   b the line that divides one country from another

3 volume
   a the number or amount of something
   b the sound level

4 species
   a animals and plants that live in a river
   b a group of animals or plants that are very similar

The Aral Sea

52

The Aral Sea

A   With 7 billion people using the world's resources, there is a lot of pressure on food and water supplies. We use water for farming, manufacturing, drinking and creating energy. The average family in the USA uses 400 gallons of water every day. People buy 240 billion litres of bottled water every year. This is putting pressure on the world's largest lakes, rivers and seas.

B   The Aral Sea sits on the border between Kazakhstan and Uzbekistan. It was once one of the largest lakes in the world. It started to get smaller from 1960. The Soviet Union started to use the water that went into the Aral Sea for farming. Now there are many smaller lakes that are not connected to the Aral Sea. There is high unemployment in the area which once had many fishermen.

C   Another great lake that is now much smaller is Lake Chad in Africa. According to the United Nations, the lake lost nearly 95 per cent of its volume between 1963 and 1998. Currently it averages just less than two metres in depth. The problem is partly caused by climate change, but has also been caused by *overgrazing, *deforestation and increased demand for water by local people.

D   Many lakes and rivers throughout the world are in danger of drying up because of the demands by people. As rivers and lakes dry, people have less water. It also means that many species of plant and animal life are dying out. People are causing the problem, but people are also suffering from the problem.

*overgrazing =   too many farm animals eating the plants from the land
*deforestation = the cutting down of forests

GRAMMAR

COUNTABLE AND UNCOUNTABLE NOUNS / *SOME* AND *ANY*

1 **Read the dictionary definitions. Then sort the words in the box into *countable* or *uncountable*.**

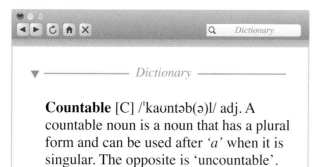

◄ ► ↻ ⌂ ✕   🔍 *Dictionary*

▼ ———————— *Dictionary* ————————

Countable [C] /ˈkaʊntəb(ə)l/ adj. A countable noun is a noun that has a plural form and can be used after '*a*' when it is singular. The opposite is 'uncountable'. *Car*, *holiday* and *bottle* are all countable nouns.

Uncountable [U] /ʌnˈkaʊntəb(ə)/ adj. An uncountable noun is a noun that has no plural form and cannot be counted in separate units. The opposite is 'countable'. *Transport*, *time* and *water* are all uncountable nouns.

---

city   advice   coffee   lecture   food   professor
job   money   flat   music   test   friend   traffic
concert   information

Countable nouns	Uncountable nouns
city	advice

2 **Read the sentences. Choose C (countable) or U (uncountable) for the nouns.**

1 There is a lot of pressure on <u>food</u> and water supplies.   C / U

2 We use <u>water</u> for farming, manufacturing, drinking and creating energy.   C / U

3 The average <u>family</u> in the US uses 400 gallons of water every day.   C / U

4 Now there are many smaller <u>lakes</u> that are not connected.   C / U

5 The problem is partly caused by climate change and less <u>rain</u>.   C / U

6 Many <u>plants</u> and animals are dying out.   C / U

3 **Complete the sentences with *some*, *any*, or *a*.**

1 Have you got _____ money?

2 We haven't got _____ water.

3 There are _____ rivers and lakes that are in danger.

4 The Aral Sea is _____ lake that is in danger.

5 There are _____ animals that are in danger.

4 **Correct the mistakes in the sentences.**

1 People are causing a damage to many rivers.

2 The weather isn't causing some of the changes.

3 Any people lost their jobs.

4 It was some good suggestions.

A

C

LISTENING

1 Label the photos with the names of the animals in activity 2.

2 🔘 36 Listen to the lecture and match the animal with the number.

1	Bald eagle	a	1500
2	Giant panda	b	10000
3	Humpback whale	c	5000
4	Grey wolf (in USA)	d	1500

3 🔘 37 Listen and complete the sentences with a number.

1 There were _____ breeding pairs of the bald eagle in the wild.
2 The population of China is over _____.
3 There were less than _____ humpback whales at one point.
4 There were no grey wolves in the _____ in America.

4 🔘 37 Listen again. Choose T (true) or F (false).

1 You cannot hunt the bald eagle in America. T / F
2 Giant pandas live in protected areas. T / F
3 You can hunt humpback whales again today. T / F
4 Grey wolves were taken from Canada to the USA. T / F

GRAMMAR

HOW MUCH / HOW MANY

1 Read the answers. Choose the correct question type.

1 I do three hours homework a day.
 How many? / How much?
2 Anne has a lot of work at the moment.
 How many? / How much?
3 There were a lot of people in the shop.
 How many? / How much?
4 The meal was very expensive.
 How many? / How much?
5 I live with two other people.
 How many? / How much?

2 Complete the short quiz with *How much* or *How many*.

1 _____ humpback whales are there in the world?
 a about 5000
 b about 14000
 c about 40000

2 _____ food does a giant panda eat every day?
 a about 20–24 kilos of bamboo shoots
 b about 6–8 kilos
 c about 9–14 kilos

3 _____ babies do grey wolves have?
 a usually 2–3
 b usually 5–6
 c usually 7–10

4 _____ does a bald eagle weigh?
 a 2–3 kilos
 b 4–6 kilos
 c 7–10 kilos

3 Now answer the questions. Write a, b or c.

1 _____ 3 _____
2 _____ 4 _____

4 Correct the mistakes in <u>three</u> of the sentences.

1 How much water does an average family use?
2 How much bottles of water do you buy every week?
3 How many species are endangered in the world?
4 How many time does it take?
5 How much countries have a dried out lake or river?
6 How many people are on your course?

VOCABULARY

WORD FORMATION

1 Complete the table with these nouns and verbs.

> destroy pollute extinction destruction
> conserve pollution conservation extinct

noun	verb

2 Complete the sentences with the verb or noun forms from activity 1.

1 The _____ of natural habitats has caused many species to die out.

2 Farms and industries _____ many rivers with chemicals.

3 Many countries try to _____ the areas where endangered animals live.

4 The _____ of different animals has happened for thousands of years.

PRONUNCIATION

1 ⊙38 **Listen to the word stress on the words in the box. Put the words in the table.**

> destroy destruction pollute pollution
> conserve conservation extinct extinction

oO	oOo	ooOo

2 ⊙38 **Listen again and repeat the words.**

Living IELTS

SAYING YOU'RE NOT SURE

1 Complete the dialogue with the sentences below.

Lucia: So, what animals are endangered in your country?

Tayo: ¹ _____

Lucia: There are lots of endangered animals.

Tayo: Which one is the most famous?

Lucia: ² _____

Tayo: Why do you think it's the brown bear?

Lucia: ³ _____

a **I guess** it's probably the brown bear.

b **I think** the rhino probably is. There aren't many left. What about in your country?

c **I'm not sure**. It's probably because there aren't many of them and they are really big and dangerous.

2 ⊙39 **Listen and check.**

3 ⊙40 **Listen and answer the questions.**

WRITING

PROBLEM-SOLUTION ESSAY

1 **Read the question and underline the key words.**

> Man is destroying Earth. Describe three ways we can stop this.

2 **Read the paragraph. Choose which ways man is destroying the Earth.**

a Eating too much meat.
b Having too many holidays.
c Using too much energy.
d Driving too much.
e Working too much.

Today, people are destroying the Earth by using resources too quickly and causing pollution. The situation needs to change quickly. We need to do three things to stop this situation. First, we need to reduce the amount of meat people eat. Second, we need to reduce the amount of energy people use. Finally, we need to work less and relax more. In this way, we can help to protect our world.

WRITING SKILLS

ORGANISING A PARAGRAPH (2)

3 **Put the functions in the correct order.**

1 why the problem exists
2 conclusion
3 three ways to solve the problem
4 the problem

4 **Put the sentences in the correct order.**

1 Firstly, we need to produce less meat and more crops. Secondly, we need to eat more local and seasonal food. Finally, better farming methods are needed.

2 More and more land is becoming poor quality and in danger of becoming a desert.

3 Making these changes will help people to protect the land.

4 This is happening because humans are farming the land too much. To solve this problem we need to take three steps.

5 **Write a paragraph. Use the model in activities 2 and 4 to help you.**

PREPARATION FOR A TEST

Preparing well for any test is important. Remember preparation isn't just revising – it's about reducing stress and helping you concentrate and study more effectively.

1   Choose Y (yes) or N (no).

> **In the final week before a test, I …**
> | | | |
> |---|---|---|
> | **1** | do exercise every day. | Y / N |
> | **2** | drink lots of water. | Y / N |
> | **3** | revise my notes and practise for the test. | Y / N |
> | **4** | eat bread, rice, pasta or cereal. | Y / N |

2   Match the points in activity 1 to the explanations below. There is more than one explanation for some points.

a This helps you to concentrate.   **c** This will make you feel less stressed.

b These give you energy slowly.   **d** The more you do something, the better your result.

3   🔘41 Read and complete the text with the words in the box below. Then listen and check.

> eat healthy food   sleep for 8 hours   take breaks   try to relax
> reward yourself   be organised and set priorities   exercise

Firstly, you need to ¹ _____. Think about what you need to study and when you need to study it. What is the most important thing for you to study? What is not very important? Make a study diary and write what you will study and when.

The next important tip is to get a good night's sleep – you need to ² _____. Then you wake up ready for a day studying. This leads me to my third tip. It's true you need to study most of the day, yes, but ³ _____. No one can study without a break for hours and hours. When you take a break, you can follow some other tips – ⁴ _____, ⁵ _____, or ⁶ _____.

Let's look at those three tips. They're really important. Exercise keeps your body fit and healthy, which will help you study. You should try to relax, so you could phone your family and friends or chat online or even have a little sleep! Next one, eat healthy food. When we're busy, it's easy to eat junk food because it's very quick. But maybe you can eat some fruit or make yourself a quick meal, like a sandwich or some pasta. This will give your body more energy to keep studying. Don't forget to ⁷ _____. For example, if you studied everything in your study diary for that day, then take the evening off. You can meet friends, go to the cinema, go shopping – do something you enjoy doing.

4   Which points in activity 3 do you do at the moment? Which would you like to use?

My goals

Choose two points to use before a test and two points to use to reduce stress. Compare them with your classmate after a test. Did the points help you? If yes, continue using them. If no, choose new ones.

Before a test	Reduce stress
1	1
2	2

WRITING TASK 2

In Section 2 of the Writing test, you have to write at least 250 words about a topic. You may have to give your opinion or suggest a solution to a problem. It's important to read the question carefully and to plan and organise your answer.

1 Read the question and the ideas below. Tick the ideas you would include and explain why.

We should not look for different sources of energy. We should change our behaviour to use less energy.
To what extent do you agree with this statement?

I would include...

1 what the different sources of energy are. ☐
2 examples of how we can change our behaviour. ☐
3 the long traffic jams in my country. ☐
4 the cost of different energy sources. ☐
5 why it's important to change our behaviour. ☐

2 Organise your ideas into four paragraphs. Complete the paragraph notes with your answers from activity 1.

1 introduction _____
2 agree _____
3 disagree _____
4 conclusion _____

3 Read the sentences and answer the questions below.

- He isn't good at languages. However, he enjoys studying them.
- My father and mother have a car. I have one too.
- Although petrol is expensive, everyone drives to work.

1 Which three words connect ideas? _____
2 Which words have a similar meaning to *and*? _____
3 Which words have a similar meaning to *but*? _____

4 Read the question in activity 1 again. Plan your answer with the stages below.

1 Think about the question and make notes about your ideas.
2 Organise your ideas into four paragraphs.
3 Include words to connect ideas in the paragraphs.

Exam Tip 👆

Complete the tips using the words in the box.

brainstorm link carefully organise

1 Read the question _____.
2 _____ your ideas first.
3 Divide and _____ your ideas into paragraphs.
4 Use suitable connecting words to _____ ideas.

Design

VOCABULARY

ADJECTIVES TO DESCRIBE OBJECTS

1 **Complete the crossword with adjectives using the clues.**

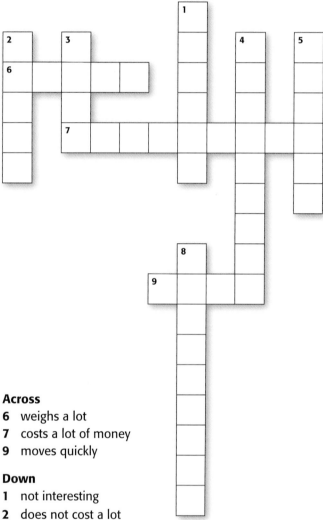

Across

6 weighs a lot
7 costs a lot of money
9 moves quickly

Down

1 not interesting
2 does not cost a lot
3 won't cause damage, harm or injury
4 works well and uses the available time, money, supplies, etc.
5 the opposite of old-fashioned
8 can harm or kill someone, or damage or destroy something

2 **Choose the correct answers.**

1 Don't watch that film in the cinema – it was really *boring / exciting*.
2 The food was nice, but it was too *expensive / cheap*. You can eat better for less money.
3 He's a very *dangerous / safe* driver. He drives carefully and very slowly.
4 These bags are really *heavy / light*. Can you help me?
5 My car is really fast, but it's very *inefficient / efficient*. I spend a lot of money of petrol.
6 I don't like *old-fashioned / modern* buildings. I prefer newer buildings like those in Dubai.
7 I haven't finished the essay. I'm so *fast / slow* doing research.

READING

1 Look at the photos. What do you know about these buildings and structures?

2 ⏱(3min) Read the text in three minutes. Match the paragraphs with the photos in activity 1.

3 Read the text again. Choose T (true) or F (false).

1 The International Space station wasn't expensive. T / F
2 The Bailong elevator is the highest in the world. T / F
3 The Bailong elevator holds a world record. T / F
4 The Alraj Al Bait Towers hold two world records. T / F
5 There is a taller building in the world than the Alraj Al bait Tower. T / F
6 The Jiazhou Bay Bridge is longer than a marathon. T / F
7 The Jiazhou bay Bridge is the longest bridge in the world. T / F

4 Complete the sentences with the words in the box.

| higher | more expensive | longer | smaller |

1 The International Space Station is _____ than the Alraj Al Bait Tower.
2 The Burj Al Khalifa elevators are _____ than the Bailong elevator.
3 The Alraj Al Bait Tower is _____ than the Burj Al Khalifa.
4 The Danyang-Kunshan Grand Bridge is _____ than the Jioazhou Bay bridge.

5 Write sentences comparing famous buildings and structures in your country with the ones in the text.

BIG PROJECTS
PAST, PRESENT AND FUTURE

Engineering projects can take years, decades, or even centuries to complete. So what are some of the record holders from around the world? And how long will they be record holders for in this world of bigger, better, faster, longer?

The International Space Station
The International Space Station is the largest spacecraft ever built. Launched in 1998, it took ten years to build. The estimated cost to build the space station is $100 billion dollars. This makes it the most expensive single object in the world.

The Bailong elevator
Back on Earth, there are lots of records for being the tallest or the highest object. One record holder is the Bailong elevator in Zhangjiajie, China. It is the world's highest and heaviest outdoor elevator, travelling to 330m. However, it isn't as high as the highest elevator in the world. The highest elevator is in the Burj Al Khalifa, in Dubai, at over 500 metres.

The Alraj Al Bait Towers
Staying in the Middle East, the Alraj Al Bait towers in Saudi Arabia hold many records, including the world's tallest hotel, the tallest clock tower and the largest clock face. It is also the second tallest building in the world, after the Burj Al Khalifa.

The Jiaozhou Bay Bridge
The world's longest bridge over the sea is the Jiaozhou Bay Bridge in China. It is 26.4 miles long. That's more than the length of a marathon! The bridge is 174 times longer than London Bridge. However, it is much shorter than the world's longest bridge. The Danyang-Kunshan Grand Bridge, in China, is more than 100 miles long and goes over land, rivers and lakes.

GRAMMAR

COMPARATIVES

1 Complete the table with the comparative forms of the adjectives below.

> big small expensive happy long good
> hot bad heavy comfortable light fast
> beautiful boring safe

add -r	
add -er	
double the final consonant and add -er	
take off the -y and add -ier	
add more	
irregular	

2 Complete the sentences with the correct form of the adjectives.

1 Are rich people _____ (happy) than poor people?
2 I need to take a _____ (long) holiday next year.
3 The buildings here are _____ (small) than in my country.
4 It's _____ (expensive) in the city than the countryside.
5 Modern buildings are _____ (comfortable) than old buildings.
6 Old materials are often _____ (heavy) than new materials.
7 This summer is _____ (hot) than last year.
8 I'd prefer a _____ (big) bedroom.

3 Read the information about two cars. Write sentences using the comparative forms of the adjectives in the box.

> efficient fast heavy light slow

	Kia Rio	Hummer H2
distance on one litre of fuel:	401.4	40.9
kilos:	1 640kg	3 000kg
top speed (kilometres per hour):	180	160

The Kia Rio is more efficient than the Hummer H2.
_____
_____
_____
_____

PRONUNCIATION

-er ENDINGS

1 🔊 42 Listen to the pronunciation of -er in comparative adjectives.

2 Circle the /ə/ sound in the comparative adjectives.

1 It's bigger than this one.
2 It's heavier than the others.
3 It's much stronger than before.
4 It older than the others.

3 🔊 42 Listen again and repeat.

Grammar

Superlatives

1 Write the superlative form of the adjectives.

1 great   *the greatest*
2 beautiful   _____
3 heavy   _____
4 tall   _____
5 expensive   _____
6 large   _____
7 long   _____
8 strong   _____
9 ugly   _____
10 bad   _____

2 Complete the sentences using your answers from activity 1.

1 It's _____ building in town. It looks horrible. Nobody likes it.
2 The Shard is _____ building in London. It's 80 metres taller than Canary Wharf.
3 The $85 billion Itaipu Dam in Brazil is _____ structure on Earth.
4 Some people think modern buildings are the best, but I don't agree. They're _____.
5 Triangles are _____ shape and help support a building.
6 I think some of _____ buildings in the world are in Paris. They look great!

3 Correct the mistake in each sentence.

1 That is the longer bridge in Mexico.
2 Mount Everest is highest mountain in the world.
3 The London Underground is the old in the world.
4 The Sahara is the bigger desert in the world.
5 Russia is biggest country in the world.
6 Kilimanjaro is the higher mountain in Africa.
7 The Shard is the taller building in London.
8 Luanda is the expensive city in the world.

LISTENING

1 Look at the photos and match each one to a decade in the box.

1950s	1960s	1970s	1980s	1990s	2000s

2 🔘 43 Listen to an interview about the different technological inventions in activity 1. Check your answers.

3 Choose the correct answers.

1 The remote control …
  a was the most important invention of the 1950s.
  b was connected to an important invention in the 1950s.

2 The inventor of the mouse made …
  a lots of money.
  b very little money.

3 The first mobile phone was … than most people's hand.
  a smaller
  b bigger

4 … made Bill Gates one of the richest men in the world.
  a Microsoft.
  b IBM.

5 The first website was built in …
  a the 1950s.
  b the 1990s.

6 Apple was …
  a clever but not rich.
  b clever and rich.

TALKING ABOUT WHAT YOU LIKE

1 🔘 44 Listen and complete the dialogue.

Lujain: Look at my new laptop! What do you think of it?

Juhaina: I like it [1] _____.

Lujain: Really? Are you sure?

Juhaina: Yes, I [2] _____ like it.

Lujain: And what about my new red headphones for the laptop?

Juhaina: I love them [3] _____.

Lujain: Good, because I [4] _____ like them.

2 Match the sentences with the functions below.

1 My other phone didn't work.
2 What do you think of my new smartphone?
3 The internet access is good – I love it.
4 I got it in the mall.

a introducing something and asking for an opinion on it
b where he/she bought it
c why he/she bought it
d why he/she likes it

B i PHONE

C MICROSOFT

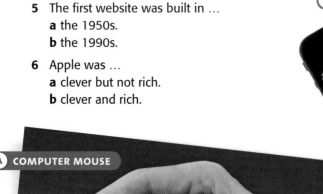

A COMPUTER MOUSE

D MOBILE PHONE

E REMOTE CONTROL

F INTERNET

WRITING

COMPARISON ESSAY

1 Read the table about new office buildings. What four points are being compared?

	Building 1	Building 2	Building 3
cost	$300 million	$200 million	$200 million
time to build	eight years	two years	three years
distance from the city centre	2 kilometres	25 kilometres	10 kilometres
people in the building	500 people	300 people	250 people

2 Read the essay. Which building does the student recommend?

The table shows three choices for a new building. The left column shows the cost, time to build, distance from the city centre and number of people each building can hold.

Building 1 can house the largest number of people. However, it is the most expensive choice and it also takes the longest time to build. Building 2 and Building 3 cost the same. However, Building 3 is smaller, takes longer to build and houses fewer people.

I think Building 1 is the best choice. It is slower to build than the others and more expensive, but it is the closest to the city centre and can hold more people.

WRITING SKILLS

FOR AND AGAINST

3 Read the essay again. Which paragraphs:

1 state the best choice?
2 describe the table?
3 compare the different choices?

4 Find the sentences in the essay that are for and the sentences that are against. Add them to the table.

for	against

THE SPEAKING TEST

1 Read the points below and circle the number which best describes you.

0 = I'm very bad at this   **2** = I'm good at this
1 = I'm not good at this   **3** = I'm very good at this

						A	B
1	I give full and developed answers.	0	1	2	3		
2	I don't memorise things to say.	0	1	2	3		
3	I don't give simple yes/no answers.	0	1	2	3		
4	I always try to give my opinion.	0	1	2	3		
5	I make notes in the one-minute preparation stage in Part 2.	0	1	2	3		
6	I use a range of grammar and vocabulary.	0	1	2	3		
7	I speak with correct intonation and try to sound interested.	0	1	2	3		
8	I ask for clarification when I don't understand.	0	1	2	3		

2 🔘45 Listen to two candidates answering Part 1 questions from the Speaking test. Tick (✔) the points in activity 1 that they are good at. Put a cross (✗) next to the points they need to improve.

3 Read the Part 1 questions from the Speaking test and then give your answers. Practise speaking aloud.

  1 Where are you from?
  2 Have you visited any English speaking countries?
  3 Why are you learning English?

4 Now read the Part 2 task card from the Speaking test. Make notes before you practise speaking aloud.

> Describe a job you would like to have. You should say:
> - what this job is
> - why you would like this job
> - what skills and qualities you need for this job
>
> And why you would like this job.

5 🔘46 Listen to an answer to the Part 2 task card. Which points in activity 1 does the candidate need to improve?

6 Use your notes from activity 4 to give your answer. Remember you have one to two minutes for this in the exam. Practise speaking aloud.

THE LISTENING TEST

1 Read the points below and circle the number which best describes you.

0 = I'm very bad at this **2** = I'm good at this
1 = I'm not good at this **3** = I'm very good at this

1	I read through the questions carefully.	0	1	2	3
2	I check the number of words I can use.	0	1	2	3
3	I try to predict the topic.	0	1	2	3
4	I try to predict the type of information in questions and gaps.	0	1	2	3
5	I understand different numbers.	0	1	2	3
6	I spell words accurately.	0	1	2	3
7	I always write an answer.	0	1	2	3
8	I move on to the next question when I can't give an answer.	0	1	2	3

2 Read the instructions and the student's answers below. Which points in activity 1 does the candidate need to improve?

> Complete the notes below. Write NO MORE THAN ONE WORD AND/OR A NUMBER for each answer.
>
> Surname: Johnson
> First names: Louise Caroline
> Address: Flat 4, 96 ¹ _Grenfild_ Avenue.
> Post code: ² _B45 2QR_
> Telephone: 01284 471147
> Mobile: ³ _0778964758_
> Date of birth: 25th ⁴ _June_ 1989.
> Start date: ⁵ _twenty-one_ May

3 🎧 47 **Listen and correct the answers.**

4 Read the tips for the speaking and listening again. Set yourself goals before the IELTS test.

My goals	How will I achieve this?
Give full and developed answers.	Practise speaking with a clock or timer and try to make my answers longer.

Plans and predictions

LISTENING

1 ⊙48 **Listen to Raouf, Sergy and Ana talking about a gap year. Match each person with the activities in the photos.**

RAOUF

A

SERGY

B

ANA

C

2 ⊙48 **Listen again. Choose Y (yes), N (no) or NG (not given).**

1 Raouf is going to cycle from Mexico City to the south of Chile. Y / N / NG
2 Raouf is going to cycle every day. Y / N / NG
3 Sergy is going to work in a bank. Y / N / NG
4 Sergy isn't going to university. Y / N / NG
5 Ana is going to spend a year climbing Kilimanjaro. Y / N / NG
6 Ana is going to travel by ferry or boat. Y / N / NG

3 **Match the people with the opinions.**

Ana   Sergy   Raouf

1 It's going to be hard. _____
2 It's going to be useful in the future. _____
3 I'm going to have experience and qualifications. _____
4 It's going to be really exciting. _____
5 It's going to be amazing. _____

4 ⊙48 **Listen again and check.**

VOCABULARY

COMMON VERB + NOUN COLLOCATIONS

1 Some verbs and nouns go together and we use them a lot in everyday English. Look at the lists below. There is one mistake in every group. Find the wrong noun and cross it out.

Take:	an exam	a gap year	a photo
	a break	a coffee	
Do:	a degree	research	a mistake
	homework	an internship	
Make:	business	money	a presentation
	friends	a plan	
Have:	a problem	fun	a decision
	a party	lunch	

2 Complete the sentences with a collocation from exercise 1. There are two sentences for every verb.

1 I'm going to _____ at a company this summer. I don't get paid but the experience is important.

2 I'm going to work for a year, so I can _____ to pay for university.

3 It's one o'clock and I'm really hungry. I'm going to _____ in the canteen.

4 We're going to _____ about conservation to our classmates tomorrow.

5 I need to study biology tonight because I'm going to _____ on Friday.

6 She's interested in chemistry, so she's going to _____ in chemical engineering next year.

7 The maths exam is going to be really easy. You're not going to _____.

8 When I go to Dubai I'm going to _____ of the Burj Khalifa Tower with my phone and send it to you.

3 Choose the correct prepositions to complete the sentences.

1 My sister's going to do research *into / for* Learning and Memory at Aberdeen University.

2 We are going to do a lot more business *with / on* China next year.

3 My class are doing presentations *into / on* student life next week.

4 I'm going to study *at / about* university in Melbourne.

5 I'm going to work *around / for* a company in Tokyo this summer.

6 A lot of my friends are going to do a degree *in / of* engineering.

4 Complete the sentences with the words in the box.

> make/earn money   make plans
> do an internship   have fun   have plans

1 I'm going to _____ at a company this summer. I won't get paid, but I'm going to get experience.

2 We aren't going to work and we aren't going to study. It's going to be like a year's holiday! We're going to _____.

3 I'm going to work for a year. I'm going to _____ to pay for university.

4 Do you _____ for the summer? I haven't got any.

5 We need to _____ for our trip to India. We're going to fly next week!

5 Choose the correct prepositions.

1 I'm going to study *at / about* university in Manchester.

2 I'm going to work *for / around* a company in Dubai this summer.

3 I'm going to stay *at / for* home for the holidays.

4 We're going to learn *about / at* management next semester.

5 They're going to travel *around / for* Europe for the summer.

6 Complete the sentences with the correct form of the words in the box.

> far off   we're off   get off

1 I'm _____ here. This is my stop.

2 _____ to work at eight o'clock.

3 We're not _____. It's only a few more minutes.

Grammar

Going to

1 Complete the questions with the correct form of *going to*.

1 What _____ you _____ do this summer?
2 Where _____ she _____ work?
3 Why _____ (not) he _____ come to the lesson?
4 How _____ we _____ get there?
5 Why _____ (not) they _____ go on holiday?

2 Match the answers to the questions in activity 1.

a She is going to work in her dad's company.
b We're going to go by train.
c I'm going to New York for a month.
d He's going to be at his grandparents' house.
e They're going to be working.

3 Correct the mistakes with the present simple in <u>three</u> of the sentences.

1 Maria going to go by car to the coast.
2 Ahmed is going to Jordan for the summer.
3 My parents is going to work this weekend.
4 Susie and Paul are going to have a great time!
5 It are going to be a difficult week.
6 The test is going to be easy.

4 Rearrange the lines to make a conversation.

Miguel:	Alex, are you going to do anything this weekend?	_1_
Alex:	Adele! I'd love to see her! She's a great singer.	____
Miguel:	I have an extra ticket. Do you want to go?	____
Alex:	No, no plans? Why? Do you have any ideas?	____
Miguel:	Well, yes. I'm going to see Adele in concert.	____
Miguel:	On Sunday evening.	____
Alex:	Sure! When is it?	____
Alex:	Oh, no, I can't! I'm going to have dinner with my classmates.	_8_

Pronunciation

Going to

1 🔊 49 Listen to six sentences. Tick the pronunciation in each sentence.

	gəʊɪŋtə	gəʊɪŋ
1		
2		
3		
4		
5		
6		

2 🔊 49 Listen again and repeat.

READING

1 Read the text and choose the best title.

1 How we can learn about IT.
2 Where will we study?
3 IT will do everything.
4 Will we travel again?

2 Read the text again and match the sentences with the paragraphs.

1 Parents won't go to see their children's teacher. ___
2 People learning Arabic will take tours by using their computer. ___
3 Students will take tests on computers. ___
4 Technology is already used by many students in the classroom. ___
5 Korean books will all be electronic in 2015. ___
6 We won't have a teacher in the classroom. ___

3 Match the words with the meanings below.

1 connect
2 virtual
3 mark
4 trip
5 tour

a to join two things together
b a journey to a place and back again
c a journey to see many places or things
d to give a score for some work
e not real

A Computers and smart boards can already be found in many classrooms. Dictionaries are often on a student's mobile phone. Many people already take notes on a tablet or laptop. In the language classroom, people no longer listen to cassettes. When are people going to stop using CDs in class?

B Students learning Arabic will have a teacher based in the Middle East. They won't be in the classroom together – they will connect on the internet. Schools won't have to go on expensive trips to other countries. They will take virtual tours of some of the most famous Arabian sites. Then they will have a conversation with Arabic students – in Arabic.

C Students won't take tests with a pen and paper. All tests will be done on a computer. They won't be marked by a teacher. The computer will mark the test. Parents will be able to download electronic copies of everything their child does.

D In South Korea, the government has said all text books will be available electronically by 2015. Some parts of the world won't take long to catch up. So how long until we will never read a paper book again?

GRAMMAR

WILL (NOT)

1 Read the text on page 95 again and underline *will* and *won't*.

2 Complete the sentences with *will* or *won't* and the verbs.

1 Computers _____ (replace) teachers. They aren't personal enough.

2 We _____ (use) computers to read in the future not books.

3 Children born in 2050 probably _____ (read) books because everything will be electronic.

4 We _____ (travel) to other countries anymore. We _____ (visit) them virtually.

5 There _____ (be) shops. We _____ (buy) everything online.

6 There _____ (be) paper money. It _____ (be) electronic.

3 Read the ways of answering a question. Then give your answers to questions 1–5.

Do you think the world will run out of oil?
Yes, I do.
No, I don't.
I'm not sure.

Do you think ...

1 the world will run out of oil?

_____

2 3D technologies will be used on all mobiles, TVs and on the internet?

_____

3 people will pay for everything with their mobile phones?

_____

4 most people will live to be 100 or older?

_____

5 people won't go to cinemas?

_____

4 Turn the questions in activity 3 into opinions.

1 Do you think the world will run out of oil?
I think the world will run out of oil.

2 _____

3 _____

4 _____

5 _____

Living IELTS

GIVING YOURSELF THINKING TIME

🔊 50 **Listen and complete the conversation.**

Nicola: What do you think the classroom will be like in the future?

Joanna: It's [1] _____ to say, but there probably won't be a classroom in the future.

Nicola: Really? Why do you think that? We will always need a teacher, won't we?

Joanna: Maybe, let me [2] _____. Well, perhaps they won't be in the classroom.

WRITING

THE FUTURE OF EDUCATION

1 Tick (✔) the statements you agree with and put a cross (✗) for the ones you don't agree with.

In the future, teachers ...	You	David	Jane
1 won't exist.			
2 won't mark student's work.			
3 will teach from home.			
4 will teach people from many different countries and schools.			

2 🔘51 Listen to David and Jane talking about the statements. Complete the table in activity 1.

3 Read the question. Who do you think would agree – David or Jane?

> In the future, teachers will be replaced by computers. Do you agree or disagree with this statement?

4 Read Jane's essay. Does she agree or disagree with the question?

> In my opinion, teachers in the future will mainly be replaced by computers. I think we will still have teachers for a few lessons, but most lessons will be online.
>
> We will have more lessons from teachers through the internet, but I don't agree that teachers will be replaced completely. I think expert teachers will teach people all around the world at the same time. I don't believe this will change the way we learn or are tested.
>
> Students will always need contact with a teacher, but maybe not in a traditional classroom. For this reason, I disagree with the statement.

WRITING SKILLS

GIVING YOUR OPINION

5 Complete the phrases.

1 In my o_____.
2 I t_____.
3 I don't a_____.
4 I don't b_____.
5 I d_____.

6 Read Jane's essay again and check your answers.

7 Rewrite these ideas about the future to give the opposite meaning.

1 In my opinion, most people will work at home in the future.
In my opinion, most people won't work at home in the future.

2 In my opinion, public libraries won't disappear in the future.
_____

3 I think checkout assistants in supermarkets will be replaced by machines.
_____

4 I don't think bicycles will replace cars in the future.
_____

5 I agree that most people will smoke cigarettes in the future.
_____

8 Read the three ways of giving your opinion on an idea. Then read the ideas below and write your opinions.

I think the world will run out of oil.
I don't agree (with that).
I agree (with that).
I'm not sure (about that).

I think:
1 public libraries will disappear.
_____

2 most people won't work at home.
_____

3 people won't smoke cigarettes any more.
_____

4 people will stop eating fish.
_____

9 Write a short essay about the question in activity 3. Use the model in activity 4 to help you.

THE WRITING TEST

1 **Read the points below and circle the number which best describes you.**

0 = I'm very bad at this   2 = I'm good at this
1 = I'm not good at this   3 = I'm very good at this

1	I manage my time well.	0	1	2	3
2	I read the question carefully and understand what I have to do.	0	1	2	3
3	I brainstorm my ideas first.	0	1	2	3
4	I write on the topic of the question.	0	1	2	3
5	I can present my opinion clearly.	0	1	2	3
6	I organise my ideas into paragraphs.	0	1	2	3
7	I can explain where the information is on a graph and what it shows.	0	1	2	3
8	I check my spelling and grammar after writing.	0	1	2	3

2 **Read the first part of an essay question and underline the key words.**

> Do the advantages of studying abroad *outweigh the disadvantages? What advice would you offer to someone planning to study abroad?

*outweigh: to be more important than

3 **Add the words in the box to the mind maps below. Add your own ideas.**

new cultures   learn a language   miss home   problems communicating
good for future job   expensive   good universities   harder work

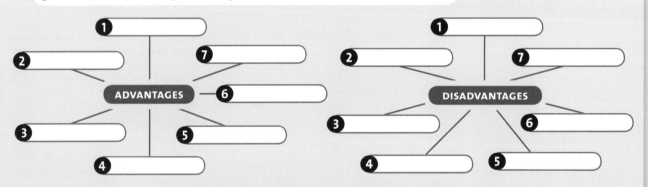

4 **Which part of the question in activity 2 does the mind map not include?**

5 **Read the sentence from an introductory paragraph. Put the other paragraphs in the correct order.**
Studying abroad is difficult at first, but the long-term advantages are very important.
Paragraph a Advice on studying abroad.
Paragraph b The difficulties of studying abroad.
Paragraph c The benefits of studying abroad.

6 **Write a short word introduction to the essay question in activity 2.**

THE READING TEST

1 Read the points below and circle the number which best describes you.

0 = I'm very bad at this   **2** = I'm good at this
1 = I'm not good at this   **3** = I'm very good at this

1	I know the different question types in the exam.	0	1	2	3
2	I manage my time well.	0	1	2	3
3	I try to predict the content from titles and opening sentences.	0	1	2	3
4	I don't waste time on words I don't know.	0	1	2	3
5	I look in the text for synonyms or ideas which appear in the questions.	0	1	2	3
6	When I can't answer a question, I move on to the next one. If I have time, I go back to the unanswered question.	0	1	2	3
7	I am confident reading different types and styles of reading text.	0	1	2	3
8	I don't worry if the text is on a topic I don't know anything about.	0	1	2	3

2 Read the title and predict the content of the text.

What will we do without oil?

3 Read the questions and underline the key words.

1 People will not take holidays in other countries so much.   Y / N / NG
2 People do not take holidays in their own country today.   Y / N / NG
3 Overseas gap years will continue.   Y / N / NG
4 People will travel less for everything.   Y / N / NG

4 Read the text and answer the questions in activity 3. Do the questions test facts or opinions?

Today, many people want more than one holiday a year, often overseas. Cheap international travel is now very popular and very easy. However, with decreasing oil supplies and the price of fuel increasing, can we continue to go to the same holiday destinations?

It is possible that new technology will allow us to travel using less oil. But until then, we need to think carefully about holiday destinations and explore our own countries. Gap years to foreign countries may not continue as flights increase in price, so young people may take gap years in their own country.

Other things will also change as fuel supplies decrease. Modern communications mean that people don't need to travel to an office for work. Children might have lessons at home, so that they don't need to travel to school. All of this could mean there will be a big change in how people travel and maybe people won't leave their own country – or their own town – in the future.

5 Read the tips for the writing and reading again. Set yourself goals before the IELTS test.

My goals	How will I achieve this?
write quicker	practise writing every day

Audioscripts

UNIT 1

Track 1

Elena: Hello, Anton!
Anton: Hi, Elena! How are you?
Elena: I'm fine, thanks. And you?
Anton: I'm very well, thanks.
Elena: Anton, this is Luc. He's from France.
Luc: Hello, Anton. Nice to meet you.
Anton: Nice to meet you, too! I'm from Russia.
Luc: Are you a new student?
Anton: Yes, I am.
Luc: I'm a new student, too!

Track 2

A: Rochila, this is Suleiman. Suleiman, this is Rochila. Rochila's a science student, too.
B: Hi, Suleiman. Nice to meet you.
C: Hello, Rochila. Nice to meet you, too.

Track 3

what　name　I

Track 4

what	stop	not	hot
name	late	hate	eight
I	fly	eye	my

Track 5

1 Let's go and say hello to Tom.
2 I meet people from my course every Friday in the café.
3 The easiest way to start a conversation in England is to talk about the weather.
4 I go out with friends after lessons.
5 I like to chat to someone new every day.

Track 6

Vera: Hi Mum, it's me, Vera.
Mum: I know it's you – no one else calls me 'Mum'! How are you?
Vera: I'm fine.
Mum: Are you eating OK?
Vera: Yes, Mum!
Mum: What's your accommodation like?
Vera: It's great. I like living in the house with Lisa, Temi and Lujain.
Mum: Tell me about your room. Is it big?
Vera: It's quite small. There isn't an armchair or a sofa in my room.
Mum: Where do you sit?
Vera: There is a sofa in the living room. There is a chair next to my desk, but it isn't very comfortable.
Mum: Do you have space for all your books?
Vera: There aren't any bookshelves, but there is a desk for my laptop.

Mum: Do you eat dinner in your room?
Vera: Mum! Food, food, food. There is a table in the living room. I eat there.
Mum: I just worry about you eating!

Track 7

Lucia

Examiner: What do you like doing in your free time?
Lucia: I like going shopping with my friends. I spend lots of time on Facebook.
Examiner: Why do you like doing these things?
Lucia: There are great shops in Bahrain. We have some really good shopping malls. There is everything you want to buy. I love Facebook. I chat there and I never text now.
Examiner: How much time do you spend on these hobbies?
Lucia: I go shopping every Saturday and often two or three nights a week. Facebook, I use all the time. I look at it on my phone, computer, laptop. I can't stop using it!
Examiner: What would you do if you had more free time?
Lucia: I want to go shopping more often, but I don't have enough money. I do have some homework to do, too.

Khalid

Examiner: What do you like doing in your free time?
Khalid: I play football three times a week. I am in the university football team. I like to meet my friends in the shopping mall at the weekends. We often go out for lunch and sometimes go to the cinema.
Examiner: Why do you like doing these things?
Khalid: I love football, it's fun to play, and it's with all my friends. It also helps me keep fit but it doesn't feel like exercise. I also love playing in the university team, we are the best in the country! The malls are great here. I don't buy many things but I like spending time with my friends.
Examiner: How much time do you spend on these hobbies?
Khalid: Football is three times a week. The games are obviously 90 minutes, but training is two hours. I spend most of the weekend in the mall.
Examiner: What would you do if you had more free time?
Khalid: I would like to go horse. I go on a horse.

UNIT 2

Track 8

Mohammed: The Scottish really enjoy New Year, don't they?
Li: Yeah. The parties are fun and the snow is beautiful.
Mohammed: What do you do in China for New Year?
Li: It's a lot more colourful. You can see it in a few weeks.
Mohammed: But it's New Year now.
Li: In China, we celebrate it at the start of spring so it's not as cold as here. It changes every year because we have a different calendar, but it's in January or February.

Mohammed: How long does it last?

Li: People do lots of things to prepare, but the main first day is New Year's Eve and it lasts for 16 days.

Mohammed: 16 days!

Li: Yes, but we don't really do anything interesting or exciting every day. New Year's Eve and New Year's Day are the most important and fun days.

Mohammed: What do you do on New Year's Eve?

Li: That's the day of the main meal. Most people eat fish and delicious dumplings. Some people eat cake.

Mohammed: What do you do on New Year's Day?

Li: People usually spend New Year's Day with their family and it is fantastic for children. They get money in red envelopes from their parents.

Mohammed: Excellent! How does it finish?

Li: Two weeks later, we have a lantern festival, but there are also lots of other traditions. There's amazing dancing, like at a carnival, and there are lots of traditional decorations and food.

Track 9

1 amazing	4 boring
2 awful	5 fantastic
3 colourful	6 exciting

Track 10

Receptionist: Good afternoon, International Business College. How can I help?

Caller: Hi, do you have any classes starting next week?

Receptionist: We do. We have one course called 'Introduction to International Business' from 7 till 9 p.m.

Caller: How much does that course cost?

Receptionist: That course is free. It's just an introduction course and a chance to find out more about our other courses.

Caller: What do we do in the class?

Receptionist: You look at some basic differences between international work and local work. You study basic cultural differences and common problems of international work.

Caller: Where does the course take place?

Receptionist: It's in Cambridge and the next one is the 29th May.

Caller: What other courses do you have?

Receptionist: We have a course called 'Working with Europe'.

Caller: How long is that course?

Receptionist: It's a four-week course.

Caller: How much does it cost?

Receptionist: It's £100 per week or £350 for the month.

Caller: What will we study?

Receptionist: In the first week, you study the European Union. In the second week, you look at logistics, in other words, transport. In weeks three and four, you study marketing and language.

Caller: Where does the course take place?

Receptionist: It's in Bury St Edmunds.

Caller: And when does it start?

Receptionist: You can start on the 29th May or the 2nd June.

Caller: Great. Could you send me some more information?

Receptionist: Sure. What's your name?

Caller: It's Mark Peace. That's M-A-R-K P-E-A-C-E.

Receptionist: And where do you live?

Caller: 20, High Street, Newmarket.

Receptionist: What's your email address?

Caller: It's m.a.peace@gmail.com.

Receptionist: Great, thank you. I'll send it through.

UNIT 3

Track 11

Max: Hi guys, how are you?

Theo: Fine.

Zara: Fine.

Max: I hate presentations! Do you, Zara?

Zara: I don't mind them. What about you, Theo?

Theo: This is my first one in English, so I'm a bit worried.

Zara: What's the topic?

Theo: It's about problems facing international students.

Max: Well, I can help with the content. I've got lots of problems!

Zara: I'm confident at talking, so I can give most of the presentation.

Theo: Really?

Zara: Sure. We give lots of presentations in Oman, so I can give the presentation.

Theo: Excellent. Well, I'm good at IT skills. I can do the PowerPoint slides.

Max: When is the presentation?

Zara: On the 20th April.

Max: I'm happy to do most of the research. I can work well alone.

Theo: OK, but we need to do it quite soon. I need to write the slides.

Zara: And I need to learn what I am saying. Let's arrange some dates to meet.

Theo: Shall we meet every Monday at 2 p.m.?

Max: That's good for me.

Zara: And me.

Theo: Great! See you all next week then.

Track 12

Georgios: I can speak English, Greek and French. I want to learn Spanish, but I can't speak it yet. How about you, Omar?

Omar: Well, I can speak English well and, of course, Arabic. I can speak Spanish, but not very well. What about computers?

Georgios: Of course I can use a computer! What about you, Omar?

Audioscripts

Omar: Sure, everyone can use a computer. What about driving?

Georgios: I'm not good at it, but I can drive.

Omar: I love driving. I can drive a car and ride a motorbike.

Georgios: There's another thing I can't do – I can't work under pressure. It makes exams really hard for me.

Omar: Really? I love pressure. It makes me work better. I can't work when there isn't pressure.

Georgios: And another thing – I can work in a team, but I prefer to work alone.

Omar: I like exams and essays, but I hate presentations, because we always have to work with other people. I can't do it very well.

Track 13

1 I can speak English.
2 Yes, I can drive a car.
3 Yes, I can.
4 I can work in a team.

Track 14

Listening

Marek: So how did you do in the listening test?

Joanna: Ok, but I made a simple mistake.

Marek: Really? What did you do?

Joanna: I copied the answers from the question sheet to the answer sheet during the test and not at the end.

Marek: Is that wrong?

Joanna: Well, I made some simple spelling mistakes. And then I didn't read the next questions, so I wasn't prepared for the next section.

Marek: So we should read the questions during the test and we should transfer the answers after the test?

Joanna: Yes. Did you make any simple mistakes?

Marek: Yes, really silly! I circled only one answer and the question needed two.

Joanna: We should read the instructions carefully.

Marek: Yes!

Reading

Joanna: What about the reading section?

Marek: I didn't answer all the questions.

Joanna: Oh no! Why?

Marek: I spent too long on one question.

Joanna: The teacher said when we don't know the answer we should leave it. But I made a silly mistake as well.

Marek: What was that?

Joanna: I wrote four or five words in the gaps. I think the instruction was no more than three words.

Marek: Yes, you shouldn't write more words than you are allowed.

Writing

Joanna: How about the writing?

Marek: My writing is too informal. The teacher said I shouldn't use too many personal pronouns. How about you?

Joanna: Mine wasn't too informal, but my vocabulary wasn't very good.

Marek: Why?

Joanna: The teacher said I shouldn't memorise lots of words without knowing how to use them.

Marek: Yes, that's good advice.

Joanna: She said it was better to use vocabulary correctly.

Speaking

Marek: How about the speaking section? I didn't say enough. I just gave one- or two-word answers.

Joanna: You should always try to give full answers.

Marek: Yes, that's what the teacher said.

Joanna: I spoke about the topic, but I forgot the points on the task card.

Marek: Oh dear. I think I did that, too.

Joanna: The teacher said we should make notes and then use the notes to help organise the talk. Then you include all the points.

UNIT 4

Track 15

1 Some of you know me – I was a student here last year. My name's Ali and now I'm studying psychology at the University of Reading, near London in the UK. I'm studying really hard but I am also having a lot of fun. It's difficult studying a degree in English and having lessons with people from all around the world, but I am learning so much. I'm making a lot of friends playing in the university football team.

2 Hi. I'm Omar, as many of you know. I'm an undergraduate student studying sociology at the University of Melbourne in Australia. I love living there and I'm making lots of friends. We study together and meet in cafés. Australia is great for sports because it's sunny but not too hot. I'm working weekends at the moment to help improve my English.

3 Hi, my name's Naif and I'm an undergraduate student on a three-year course studying Law. My brother is studying a one-year postgraduate course at the same university, so we are living together. I'm hoping to stay and also study a postgraduate course in Law. I go shopping most weekends and walking in the park, because the weather is so good. Oh, I'm also studying in Australia but I'm studying in Sydney.

Track 16

geology   literature   languages   sociology
psychology   biology

Track 17

1 1.4
2 7
3 22 000
4 1.2
5 63
6 1 200

Track 18

1.8   8 500   800   2.7   2 600   1 800
2.3   150   15 280

UNIT 5

Track 19

Ibrahim: Thanks so much for inviting me to Beijing! This has to be one of the best things about being an international student!

Ming: What?

Ibrahim: Travelling all over the world to see your friends. You should come to Dubai next.

Ming: That would be great!

Ibrahim: Wow! What is that?!

Ming: That's what I wanted to show you. It's the national stadium.

Ibrahim: When did they finish it?

Ming: They finished it for the Olympics in 2008.

Ibrahim: The design is fantastic! It's so modern. How did they decide on the design?

Ming: Architects designed models and this was the one the judges liked the best.

Ibrahim: Did it take long to construct?

Ming: They started in 2003 and over 17 000 builders worked on it.

Ibrahim: It looks expensive!

Ming: It was cheaper than they planned. They wanted a roof, but they decided not to build a roof and they saved $200million.

Ibrahim: That's amazing! Can we go inside?

Ming: Sure. I booked a tour.

Track 20

1 arrived
2 needed
3 stopped
4 started
5 watched
6 used
7 worked

UNIT 6

Track 21

Karen: What modules are you going to take next semester?

Leandro: I'm not sure yet, but I went to a talk this morning on a really interesting module.

Karen: Really? What was it?

Leandro: It's called 'student enterprise'. Geraldine did it last year.

Karen: Did she enjoy it?

Leandro: Yes, she did. She said it was the best module she did.

Karen: What did she do on the module?

Leandro: She started her own business in a team with other students.

Karen: Really? What did they sell?

Leandro: They sold doughnuts!

Karen: Why did they do that?

Leandro: They had to make a profit selling something. Students always buy junk food!

Karen: And this is a module? I can use it as part of my degree?

Leandro: Yes. You have to write a business plan, organise your team, manage the business and write a report about it.

Karen: It sounds like good fun.

Leandro: It is.

Karen: Did Geraldine tell you that?

Leandro: No, I spoke to one of the people from last year. They were at the talk.

Karen: Did they give you any ideas for the business?

Leandro: No, you can do anything. Do you want to do it together?

Karen: OK, great idea. What shall we do?

Track 22

1 confident
2 well-paid
3 meet
4 read
5 welcome
6 answer

Track 23

Ahmed: It must be so easy for you going to university in your own country.

Bruce: It probably is easier than being in a different country, but some things are hard.

Ahmed: What do you find difficult?

Bruce: Well, at school I had deadlines; I was good at organising time. Well, my teachers and parents helped me. But it's harder at university because I have to manage my own time.

Ahmed: I see. Is it really difficult?

Bruce: Yes, really! Time management is important. There are three things I try to do now. Firstly, I try to set clear times between free-time and independent study.

Ahmed: But they're the same thing, aren't they?

Bruce: No, they aren't. I put independent study into my schedule. It's the same with deadlines.

Ahmed: What do you mean?

Bruce: Well, the teachers give us an essay title three of four weeks before the deadline. I try to manage my time and have a goal for every week. For example, I finish background reading on the essay in the first week. Then I start a draft in the second week.

Ahmed: So you're more responsible now?

Bruce: Yes, exactly. I'm responsible for my learning goals. It's my degree and it's my future.

UNIT 7

Track 24

1 I have to go now!
2 I don't have to, but I want to read this essay tonight.
3 Yes, you have to do your homework.
4 I collected the books, so you don't have to.

Audioscripts

Track 25

Alice: I need to get fit! I'm so unhealthy! I feel terrible just walking up the stairs!

Tom: You should get some Kangoo jumps.

Alice: Some what? Kangaroo jumps?

Tom: No, these.

Alice: What are they?

Tom: They are Kangoo jumps.

Alice: They look dangerous. I want to get fit, not break my bones!

Tom: They are actually good for your bones. Running can be bad for your bones on a hard path or road. These help your bones.

Alice: Really? How do you use them?

Tom: You can use them running, jogging, walking or doing an exercise class.

Alice: But I can do those anyway. Why do I need these shoes?

Tom: You don't need them, but they make boring exercise more fun.

Alice: I do hate running and jogging.

Tom: Me too.

Alice: But are they better for you?

Tom: Well, some studies show that your lungs get stronger quicker with these than normal running. You will get fit faster!

Alice: Really?!

Tom: They also help to prevent injuries.

Alice: I always get injured when I start sports.

Tom: That's because you never do any! These will help you get fit and give you less chance of injury.

Alice: I think I'll get some. You have to run with me though. I'll look like an idiot!

Tom: You won't. It's fun!

Track 26

Andre: There are so many words to remember!

Carole: I know! It's really hard. What do you do to remember vocabulary?

Andre: I like to put words into groups.

Carole: What do you mean?

Andre: Well, I write a topic in the middle of a page. For example, 'adjectives to describe places'. Then every time I hear a new word for that topic I add it to the group. It helps me to remember more words. How about you?

Carole: I like to make a link to a picture.

Andre: What do you mean? Do you draw every word?

Carole: No, sometimes I draw something, but often I just remember a picture of something connected to the word.

Andre: That wouldn't help me. But it does help me when I hear a word. I often say words aloud to myself.

Carole: Yes, that's a good idea. I think it's important to write sentences using the word, too. The meaning is only one thing; we have to learn how to use the words in sentences as well.

Track 27

Chen Chen

I think the Forbidden City is one of the most important historical buildings in China. It's nearly 600 years old and for 500 years it was the home of different emperors in China. The first emperors from the Ming dynasty lived there in 1420, and over 20 other emperors lived there after that. The last emperor was in 1912 and he left the palace in 1924. Oh, it's in Bejing. It's now an important and popular place for tourists. Sorry, do you know where Beijing is? No? It's in the North of China. It's the capital city. I think it's an important building in China. I like it a lot because it shows the world our history. China is an old country and the emperors were part of this history. It's near my house. It's a short drive.

Juan

I'm from Peru, so the important place is definitely Machu Picchu. It's really old and the tourists love the city. People forgot about it, but then an American explorer visited and then everyone in the world knew about it. The buildings are in the hills in Peru. Many people think they are important. We have lots of tourists visiting.

UNIT 8

Track 28

Halide: Have you booked a holiday yet?

Nori: I have. I'm going to America!

Halide: Excellent. Have you been before?

Nori: Yes, I went to New York two years ago.

Halide: I was in New York last year. Where are you going this time?

Nori: I've booked a month's holiday in California.

Halide: California! I love California. I went there when I was a child. Where are you going?

Nori: I haven't decided exactly. I haven't read much yet.

Halide: But you must know where you are staying?

Nori: No. I've hired a car, so I can go where I want!

Halide: Oh wow! Such freedom. Have you been on a driving holiday before?

Nori: No, I haven't.

Halide: You'll love it. I went on a driving holiday four years ago when I was a student. I went with friends to Australia. It was wonderful. So have you booked any hotels?

Nori: No, I haven't. I need to find one for LA when I land. After that, I don't mind.

Halide: What do you want to do there?

Nori: I haven't got many plans, but I want to spend a few days skiing.

Halide: Have you skied before?

Nori: No, I haven't. This will be my first time. Have you skied before?

Halide: I have. I went skiing last winter for the first time.

Nori: You've done everything!

Track 29

1 **A:** I'm going to Hawaii next week.
 B: Hawaii!? Wow! That sounds great!
 A: Yeah! And I'm going surfing.
 B: Surfing! That sounds exciting!
 A: Yeah, I can't wait!

2 **A:** I'm going to Jeddah next week.
 B: Jeddah! Wow! That sounds exciting!
 A: Yeah! And I'm going scuba diving.
 B: Scuba diving! That sounds great!
 A: Yeah, I can't wait!

Track 30

1 Have you ever been to Madagascar?
2 Yes, I have.
3 Has he ever seen a lemur?
4 No, he hasn't.

Track 31

Teacher: This is a good essay Luca. Well done! There are some mistakes.

Luca: Could you show me, Miss?

Teacher: Sure. The first problem is that your ideas are good but not very well organised. Try to make every paragraph about just one topic.

Luca: So here, for example, it should be two paragraphs?

Teacher: Exactly. Also, pay attention to your grammar. You use the past simple a lot, but you need the present perfect in this sentence.

Luca: I find the present perfect really hard.

Teacher: It is difficult, but practise with your grammar exercise book.

Luca: Is there anything else?

Teacher: Well, your spelling needs to improve.

Luca: How can I improve my spelling, Miss?

Teacher: Reading is really important because it helps you see the patterns of words. And keep a vocabulary notebook to help you remember the spelling, too.

Luca: OK, great. Thank you, Miss.

Track 32

1 There are 50 people in each class.
2 I live at number 116.
3 The train leaves at twenty to three.
4 The course starts on the seventh.
5 A ticket costs £53.
6 My number is 777289.
7 I weigh 58 kilos.
8 Her mobile number is 07889 47 11 47.

Track 33

Student: Hi, I'm phoning to find out about the activities for the first day.

Receptionist: Sure. Come to the school before 9 o'clock. Come to reception and we'll register you on the course.

Student: And then do classes start?

Receptionist: No, there aren't any classes on the first day. At 9.30, we'll go to the main hall and you'll meet the teachers and the director.

Student: What will we do for the rest of the day?

Receptionist: After you have met the teachers and director, there will be a test at 10.30.

Student: Where will the test be?

Receptionist: In the library.

Student: What will the test be?

Receptionist: It's an English test.

Student: OK, great, thank you. How can I find the main hall?

Receptionist: Go straight down the corridor past the staff room on the left. At the end of the corridor turn left. Go past the toilet and the canteen and at the end of the corridor is the main hall.

Student: Do we get a break after the talk?

Receptionist: You can have a short break. You can go to the canteen or opposite the staff room is a classroom. The classroom is next to the reception.

Student: How can I find the library later?

Receptionist. If you are in the classroom, go to the end of the corridor and turn right. Go past the self-access centre and at the end of the corridor is the library.

Student: Great, thank you.

UNIT 9
Track 34

Twins are not very common throughout the world. Think back to your school and childhood – how many twins did you know? Most of us knew one, maybe two, sets of twins when we were young.

So, an Indian village where there are 220 sets of twins in just 2 000 families is interesting for scientists. Experts visited the remote tropical village of Kodinhi, which is located in Kerala. It had almost six times as many twins as the average number.

More and more twins are born in the village every year. In 2008, 15 pairs of twins were born in the village out of a total of 300 babies. 220 sets of twins are registered in the village. However, not all parents register their children, so we don't know exactly how many twins there are. Some people think there might be 350 sets of twins. In a village of 2 000, that means one third are twins.

Dr Sribiju, a local doctor, thinks it started 60 to 70 years ago. At the moment no one knows why there are so many twins, but Dr Sribiju thinks it is the food and drink that the villagers have.

Asian people often have the lowest number of twins in the world. They usually have just four twins in 1 000 births. It is usually older women that have twins, but the average age of mothers in Kodinhi is 18 to 20 years old. Also, women over 5ft 3in tall are more likely to have twins and the average height in Kodinhi is 5ft.

It is hoped that more research can be done to find out why this is happening in such a small town.

Audioscripts

Track 35

1 A: I didn't know anything about the topic and I got nervous, and then I found the paragraph matching really difficult.

B: You don't need to know everything about the topic. Don't worry. Try reading the first sentence of each paragraph because it has the main idea. It'll help you understand the paragraph and the text.

2 C: How was the test?

D: I didn't answer a lot of the questions.

C: The multiple choice ones?

D: Yes.

C: The questions are in the same order as the text.

D: So?

C: Well, for example, the answer for number three will be between the answers for two and four in the text. You should make a guess anyway – you could be right!

D: Yes, I suppose so.

3 E: I read the text first.

F: I read all the questions first.

E: Really? Why do you do that?

F: Short-answer questions usually test details. So it's good to know what you're looking for.

4 G: I'm really worried. I couldn't find the answer to three of the questions. I spent a long time trying to find the answers.

H: When you can't find an answer, it probably means it is not given.

G: What does that mean?

H: It means that the information isn't in the text.

UNIT 10

Track 36

The bald eagle is not in danger today. In 1940, the American government banned the hunting of the bald eagle and it has successfully grown in numbers. There are now 10 000 breeding pairs in the wild.

The giant panda has not been so successful. Although some numbers are as high as 3 000, not everyone agrees. The numbers are now around 1 500 in the wild. The pandas have been protected by conserving and protecting the area they live in.

In the 1940s, humpback whale numbers were very low. But after people stopped hunting the animals in 1963, the numbers grew to around 40 000. Although it is still banned all over the world, some countries have started to hunt again.

In certain parts of America, there were no grey wolves in the early part of the 20th century. However, in the 1990s wolves were flown in from Canada and re-introduced. Now there are up to 5 000 in America.

Track 37

At one point, the bald eagle had a population of only 417 breeding pairs due to shooting, changes to its

habitat, and damage caused by an insecticide called DDT. Insecticides are used by farmers to kill insects.

The giant panda really suffered as the population of China grew – there are now over 1.3 billion people. People destroyed the area the panda lived in and the food it ate. For these reasons, numbers fell to around 1 500 in the wild.

The humpback whale was hunted like the bald eagle. People wanted its meat. About 80 years ago it was hunted so much that the population fell to less than 2 000.

The grey wolf was also under threat. It has a very large population in some parts of the world today. However, in the USA, hunting destroyed the population completely in the lower states. There were none left in America by the 1930s.

Track 38

destroy	conserve
destruction	conservation
pollute	extinct
pollution	extinction

Track 39

Lucia: So, what animals are endangered in your country?

Tayo: I think the rhino probably is. There aren't many left. What about in your country?

Lucia: There are lots of endangered animals.

Tayo: Which one is the most famous?

Lucia: I guess it's probably the brown bear.

Tayo: Why do you think it's the brown bear.

Lucia: I'm not sure. It's probably because there aren't many and they are really big and dangerous.

Track 40

1 So, what animals are endangered in your country?

2 Which one is the most famous?

3 Why do you think that?

Track 41

Firstly, you need to be organised and set priorities. Think about what you need to study and when you need to study it. What is the most important thing for you to study? What is not very important? Make a study diary and write what you will study and when.

The next important tip is to get a good night's sleep – you need to sleep for eight hours. Then you wake up ready for a day studying. This leads me to my third tip. It's true you need to study most of the day, yes, but take breaks. No one can study without a break for hours and hours. When you take a break, you can follow some other tips – exercise, try to relax, or eat healthy food.

Let's look at those three tips. They're really important. Exercise keeps your body fit and healthy, which will help you study. You should try to relax, so you could phone your family and friends or chat online or even have a little sleep! Next one, eat healthy food. When we're busy, it's easy to eat junk food because it's very quick.

But maybe you can eat some fruit or make yourself a quick meal, like a sandwich or some pasta. This will give your body more energy to keep studying. Don't forget to reward yourself. For example, if you studied everything in your study diary for that day, then take the evening off. You can meet friends, go to the cinema, go shopping – do something you enjoy doing.

UNIT 11

Track 42

1 It's bigger than this one.
2 It's heavier than the others.
3 It's much stronger than before.
4 It's older than the others.

Track 43

Interviewer: So what do you think was the most important technological invention of the 1950s?

Interviewee: Well, the thing that really changed everyday life in America was the TV, because everyone started to buy one. It wasn't invented in the 1950s, but TVs became popular then because they were cheap. So, the invention I've chosen is connected to the TV – it's the remote control. It's not really the greatest invention, but it's linked to an important invention that changed daily life.

Interviewer: Which invention do you think was ahead of its time in the 1960s?

Interviewee: Well, this is an interesting one. It's the computer mouse. In many countries you have to get a patent when you invent something new. This means you make money every time someone sells your invention. Douglas Engelbart invented the computer mouse way back in 1963. However, even in the mid-1980s many people did not use a mouse. The mouse only really became widely used in the 1990s. A patent in America only lasts 20 years, so Engelbart didn't make much money from his invention.

Interviewer: So how about the 1970s?

Interviewee: It has to be cell phone or the mobile phone. The first phone was bigger than your hand and nearly as big as your head. Motorola changed the way we live and work with mobile technology.

Interviewer: So did this technology continue in the 1980s?

Interviewee: It did continue, but the main thing for me in the 1980s was Microsoft. Its success made Bill Gates the richest man in the world for many years. It's on so many PCs that it has to be one of the greatest inventions.

Interviewer: Well, moving onto the 1990s – which invention would you choose then?

Interviewee: It has to be the internet. Like so many great things, it is difficult to say that one person in one year invented it. The internet was around in the 1950s, but the internet, as we know it now, became really popular in the 90s. Tim Berners-Lee, a British physicist, built the first website in 1990.

Interviewer: So finally the 2000s?

Interviewee. This is where the mobile phone comes back. Who would have thought that the Motorola mobile of the 1970s would become the iPhone of 2007? Apple was one of the cleverest companies of the decade and became one of the richest.

Track 44

Lujain: Look at my new laptop! What do you think of it?
Juhaina: I like it a lot.
Lujain: Really? Are you sure?
Juhaina: Yes, I really like it.
Lujain: And what about my new red headphones for the laptop?
Juhaina: I love them so much.
Lujain: Good, because I really like them.

Track 45

Candidate A

1 **Interviewer:** Where are you from?
  Candidate A: I'm from Berlin.
2 **Interviewer:** Have you visited any English-speaking countries?
  Candidate A: I haven't been to any English-speaking countries. I'd love to go to Australia, but my family usually take holidays in countries in Asia, like Cambodia, Thailand and Malaysia. It means I have to use my English a lot though, as we go abroad every year.
3 **Interviewer:** Why are you learning English?
  Candidate A: For my studies.

Candidate B

1 **Interviewer:** Where are you from?
  Candidate B: I'm from Cologne. It's a large city in the west of Germany close to the Dutch and Belgian borders. It's not the most famous city in Germany, but lots of people know it for its carnival and markets.
2 **Interviewer:** Have you visited any English-speaking countries?
  Candidate B: Yes, America.
3 **Interviewer:** Why are you learning English?
  Candidate B: I'm going to university in the UK next year, so I need to improve my English. I also think it will help me to get a job in the future. And anyway it's helpful in life in general. So many people communicate in English.

Track 46

I want to be a doctor when I finish university. I think it is good to have a job that helps people. I want to help people. You need to be intelligent and caring to be a doctor. I am intelligent and caring. Yes, I want to be a doctor.

Track 47

Receptionist: Hello, Top Gym. How can I help?
Louise: Hi, I'd like to join the gym, please.

Receptionist: Certainly. I'll take some details and then I'll send you the membership form. Could you tell me your family name?

Louise: Sure, my family name is Johnson and my first names are Louise Caroline.

Receptionist: And your address please?

Louise: It's Flat 4, 96 Greenfield Avenue.

Receptionist: Sorry, what was that?

Louis: Greenfield. G-R-E-E-N-F-I-E-L-D.

Receptionist: Great, thank you. And could you tell me the postcode please?

Louise: It's P54 2QR.

Receptionist: Could I also take your phone number?

Louise: It's 01284 471147, and my mobile number is 07889 64758.

Receptionist. Thank you. Just two more things. Could I ask for your date of birth?

Louise: Yes, it's the 25th of June 1989.

Receptionist: And when would you like to start your membership?

Louise: Could I start this month?

Receptionist: Of course. What date would you like to start?

Louise: Could I start on the 21st?

Receptionist: Certainly. I'll get the form in the post to you.

UNIT 12

Track 48

Interviewer: Many people think of a gap year as a long holiday, but a lot of people on gap years choose to make money for charity or to work. I'm joined by three people who are going to have very busy gap years. So, Raouf, what are you going to do for your gap year?

Raouf: I'm going to cycle from Mexico City to the south of Chile.

Interviewer: Wow! That's going to be tough. How long are you going for?

Raouf: We're going to go for a year. It's going to be hard. We're going to cycle 8500km in total.

Interviewer: How many kilometres are you going to cycle every day?

Raouf: We have to cycle 25 every day, but we are going to cycle more some days.

Interviewer: You're going to need a break!

Raouf: That's true, but it's going to be really exciting. It's going to be an adventure of a lifetime!

Interviewer: Nowhere quite so exotic for you, Sergy!

Sergy: No, I'm going to work for a year.

Interviewer: What are you going to do?

Sergy: I'm going to work in a bank. I'm going to save money to pay for university.

Interviewer: What are you going to do in the bank?

Sergy: Nothing very interesting. I'm going to have an office job. I hope it's going to be useful in the future.

Interviewer: How?

Sergy: Well, so many people graduate with degrees. I hope it's going to make me look different. I'm going to have qualifications and experience.

Interviewer: Now back to the exotic! Kilimanjaro for you, Ana.

Ana: Yes. We're going to climb Kilimanjaro for charity.

Interviewer: How high are you going to climb?

Ana: It's nearly 6000 metres.

Interviewer: That's not going to take a year!

Ana: No, I'm also going to work in a nature reserve. It's going to be amazing working with the animals.

Track 49

1 We're going to be late.
2 We're going to have a great time.
3 They're going out tonight.
4 She's going away.
5 I'm going to leave now.
6 They're going on holiday.

Track 50

Nicola: What do you think the classroom will be like in the future?

Joanna: It's hard to say, but there probably won't be a classroom in the future.

Nicola: Really?! Why do you think that? We'll always need a teacher, won't we?

Joanna: Maybe. Let me think. Well, perhaps they won't be in the classroom.

Track 51

David: So, what do you think? Will teachers exist?

Jane: Of course they will!

David: I don't know. We already have lectures online sometimes.

Jane: Yes, by teachers.

David: But once the lectures are recorded, teachers aren't needed.

Jane: Who will mark the work?

David: Maybe computers will.

Jane: I don't think computers will mark essays. They won't be that intelligent.

David: Teachers use computers all the time anyway. So, do you think they will teach from home?

Jane: No, they won't. We'll still go to lessons. I know you don't like lessons, but you will have to go!

David: You're probably right. Will they teach people in other countries?

Jane: Yes, I think they will sometimes.

David: Me too.

Answer Key

UNIT 1

LISTENING

1
5 **Elena:** Hello, Anton!
10 **Anton:** Hi, Elena! How are you?
6 **Elena:** I'm fine, thanks. And you?
9 **Anton:** I'm very well, thanks.
1 **Elena:** Anton, this is Luc. He's from France.
7 **Luc:** Hello, Anton. Nice to meet you.
2 **Anton:** Nice to meet you too! I'm from Russia.
4 **Luc:** Are you a new student?
8 **Anton:** Yes, I am.
3 **Luc:** I'm a new student too!

LIVING IELTS

1
1 this is
2 this is
3 to meet you
4 you too

GRAMMAR

1
1 We are students.
2 I am from Germany.
3 They are from Greece.
4 She is French.
5 London is in the UK.
6 I am her brother.

2
1 ~~isn't~~ aren't
2 ~~are~~ is
3 ~~are~~ isn't, ~~are~~ is
4 ~~is~~ am
5 ~~aren't~~ isn't
6 ~~be~~ isn't

3
1 b 2 a 3 d 4 c 5 e

PRONUNCIATION

2
/ɒ/: stop, not, hot
/eɪ/: late, hate, eight
/aɪ/: fly, eye, my

VOCABULARY

1
1 say
2 meet
3 start
4 go out
5 chat

READING

1
1 They live at home.
2 Because the windows are small.
3 It can be very noisy.
4 They could rent a house or a private bedsit or flat.
5 You meet some of the best friends you make in your life. You have fun meeting people from around the world.

2
1 small   4 uncomfortable
2 dark   5 noisy
3 hot

VOCABULARY

1 flat
2 house
3 bedsit
4 student hall
5 comfortable
6 cold
7 untidy

LISTENING

1
1 bed   5 sofa
2 laptop   6 window
3 lamp   7 bookshelves
4 desk   8 table

2
1 mother   3 house
2 food   4 A

3
1 armchair, sofa
2 sofa
3 chair
4 bookshelves, desk
5 table

GRAMMAR

1
1 is   3 is
2 are   4 are

2
1 Are there
2 Are there
3 Is there
4 Are there
5 Is there

3
There is a shopping centre.
There isn't a restaurant.
There are two banks.
There isn't a café.
There are two supermarkets.
There isn't a post office.
There is a doctor's.

WRITING

1
1 There are four courses at the university.
2 There are 350 students in the university.
3 There is a library.
4 Yes, there is a telephone in every bedroom.
5 Yes, there are lots of restaurants.

2
1 What is your name?
2 Where are you from?
3 What is your home near?/What is near your home?
4 What is your home like?
5 How many people live in your town?
6 What do you do in the evenings?

3
a 3 b 1 c 6 d 4 e 5 f 2

EXAM SKILLS

3
Khalid

4
Question 1   Lucia
Question 2   Lucia
Question 3   Khalid
Question 4   Khalid

EXAM TIP

1 full   3 understand
2 clearly   4 synonym

UNIT 2

READING

1 c

2
1 three weeks
2 dance, theatre, music, exhibitions and events
3 1947
4 perform

3
1 show   4 famous
2 programme   5 performs
3 festivals

GRAMMAR

1
1 ~~comes~~ come
2 ~~goes~~ go
4 ~~likes~~ like
5 ~~live~~ lives
7 ~~visits~~ visit

Answer Key

2

2 A lot of tourists go to Edinburgh in August.
3 Most people enjoy music.
4 She eats meat.
5 The show starts at 11.45.
6 Sally listens to traditional Scottish music.
7 I live near my family.
8 We have a holiday every year.

Listening

1

1 Spring
2 16 days
3 New Year's Eve and New Year's Day

2

1 different
2 family
3 fish
4 red

Living IELTS

1

Paul likes football.
Paul hates fish.
Katrina doesn't like Carnival.
Katrina loves football.
Katrina likes fish.

Vocabulary

1

1 awful a, amazing b
2 delicious a, interesting b
3 boring a, beautiful b
4 colourful a, exciting b
5 fantastic a, freezing b

2

1 boring
2 amazing
3 awful
4 colourful
5 delicious

Pronunciation

1

1 three   4 two
2 two   5 three
3 three   6 three

3

amazing   boring
awful   fantastic
colourful   exciting

Grammar

1

1 a   2 a   3 b   4 a   5 a   6 b

2

1 ~~Do~~ Does he speak Spanish?
3 ~~Does~~ Do they enjoy learning English?
4 ~~Does~~ Do we have homework?

3

1 How long   3 Where
2 When   4 What

4

1 b   2 c   3 e   4 d   5 a

Writing

1

1 the first of May
2 traditional music and dancing
3 Labour Day

2

May Day happens on the first of May in England. It happens every year and it is traditionally celebrated at the end of winter. There is a May Queen and traditional dancing. In Oxford it is traditional to meet at 6 a.m. outside Magdalen College. At Durham University students enjoy folk dancing and traditional music. It is called Labour Day in many other countries, such as Germany, Bahrain and Brazil.

3

1 capital letter   3 months, places
2 full stop

4

happens   celebrate
is   remembers
lasts

Study Skills

3

1 The student wrote more than three words.
2 The student wrote the answer not the letter.
3 The student chose two answers not one.
4 The student chose one answer not two.

Exam Skills

1

1 A man is booking a course.
2 no more than three
3 yes

2

1 What … ? When … ?
2 What … ?
3 What … ?
4 How long … ?
5 How much … ?
6 What … ?

7 When … ?
8 What … ?
9 What … ? / Where … ?
10 What … ?

3

1 7 / seven
2 differences
3 Working with Europe
4 four / 4 weeks
5 £100 per week
6 language
7 2 May / second of May
8 Mark Peace
9 20, High Street
10 m.a.peace@gmail.com

4

1 accommodation
2 acceptable
3 argument
4 calendar
5 until
6 relevant

5

1 brief, amount
2 advertisement, separate
3 environment, teacher
4 believe, benefit
5 column, their
6 schedule, pronunciation

Exam Tip

1 instructions   3 type
2 number   4 spelling

UNIT 3

Vocabulary

1

1 friendly   4 sad
2 intelligent   5 warm
3 nervous   6 happy

2

1 quiet   4 talkative
2 shy   5 confident
3 lazy   6 hardworking

Listening

1

Presentation topic: problems facing international students
Presentation date: 20th April
Date of meetings: Monday at 2 p.m.

2

1 b   2 a   3 c

Grammar

1

1 never   4 usually
2 sometimes   5 always

2

1 We often have to work in teams at university.
2 I sometimes give presentations.
3 The lecturers usually give us a test at the end of the year.
4 We never have a multiple choice test – it is always essays.

3

1 often   4 usually
2 always   5 never
3 sometimes

READING

1

1 A 2 A 3 B

2

1 dominate   4 share
2 develop   5 an agenda
3 role

GRAMMAR

1

1 can   4 can
2 can't   5 can't
3 can

2

Ciara

3

1 Ciara   4 can
2 can   5 can't
3 can   6 can

READING

1

1 Giuseppe
2 Anastasia
3 Giuseppe
4 Giuseppe
5 Anastasia
6 Giuseppe

PRONUNCIATION

1

	Georgios	Omar
speak Spanish	✗	✓
use a computer	✓	✓
drive	✓	✓
work under pressure	✗	✓
work in a team	✓	✗

2

1 weak   3 strong
2 weak   4 weak

WRITING

1

1 Yes, they do.
2 No, they don't. They listen to employees.
3 Good leaders need communication, listening and decision-making skills.

2

1 and   3 too
2 and, also

3

Some people think leaders **and** managers are different. Managers make simple decisions but leaders **also** motivate people to work hard. Leaders don't only make decisions – people want to follow them **too**.

4

1 and   3 and
2 also   4 too

STUDY SKILLS

1

1 four
2 an essay
3 four
4 three
5 a two-way discussion

2

1 read   6 pronouns
2 transfer   7 use
3 read   8 full
4 spend   9 points
5 write

EXAM SKILLS

1

1 b 2 b 3 a

2

1 b 2 b 3 b

4

yes

EXAM TIP

1 technique   3 text
2 questions   4 order

UNIT 4

VOCABULARY

1

1 Geology
2 Literature
3 Maths
4 Computer Science
5 Business
6 Law
7 Engineering
8 Medicine
9 Languages
10 Sociology
11 Psychology
12 Biology

2

1 biology   7 languages
2 literature   8 geology
3 maths   9 computer science
4 business   10 law
5 Sociology   11 engineering
6 psychology   12 medicine

3

1 higher education
2 degree
3 qualification
4 pass

LISTENING

1

1 Ali, Omar and Naif
2 their school
3 their university studies
4 subject and country of study

2

Ali = Psychology, UK
Omar = Sociology, Australia
Naif = Law, Australia

3

Ali = 2
Omar = 2
Naif = 1 and 2

PRONUNCIATION

1

● ○ ○	○ ● ○ ○	○ ○ ● ○ ○
literature languages	geology psychology biology	sociology

GRAMMAR

2

2 I am doing   5 I am thinking
3 I am taking   6 I am looking
4 I am hoping

3

1 Who are you living with?
2 Are you working hard?
3 Do you like living in Australia?
4 What modules are you studying for Sociology?
5 Why are you hoping to study a postgraduate course?
6 Are you enjoying living with British students?

Answer Key

4
a 6   b 2   c 4   d 1   e 3   f 5

READING

1
1 no
2 1.7 per cent
3 France
4 a study abroad programme
5 over 10 000

2
1 that they study in western-style countries
2 Chinese
3 2 600
4 Europe

3
1 western
2 global
3 overseas
4 campuses

PRONUNCIATION

1
1 a   2 b   3 b   4 a   5 b   6 b

GRAMMAR

1
1 is studying   4 go
2 are studying   5 am living
3 are taking   6 learn

2
1 C is going down.
2 B is staying the same.
3 A is going up.

WRITING

1
1 bar chart
2 going down
3 less

2
1 line graph
2 On the left
3 is increasing
4 less

3
1 line graph
2 full-time first degrees
3 years
4 subject (area)
5 is increasing
6 is becoming

EXAM SKILLS

1
1 c   2 a   3 d   4 b

2
1 internet shoppers by age group
2 the different age of the shoppers
3 left/vertical/y
4 4 (1995, 2000, 2005, 2010)

3
1 b   2 a

4
Going up: increasing, growing, rising
Going down: decreasing, falling

EXAM TIP

1
1 type
2 important
3 trends

UNIT 5

VOCABULARY

1
1 tall, glass
2 modern, ugly
3 wonderful, fantastic/fantastic, wonderful
4 brick
5 unusual

2
A glass, ugly, modern, tall, huge, unusual, fantastic, wonderful
B stone, glass, ugly, modern, concrete, unusual, fantastic, brick, wonderful
C old, stone, glass, ugly, tall, unusual, fantastic, wonderful
D glass, ugly, modern, concrete, tall, huge, unusual, fantastic, wonderful
E old, stone, ugly, modern, concrete, tall, huge, unusual, fantastic, brick, wonderful

READING

1
1 T   2 F   3 F   4 F   5 T
6 T   7 T   8 T   9 T   10 T

3
1 A   2 A   3 B   4 A

GRAMMAR

1
1 1896   3 200
2 1920   4 China

2
1 was   7 was
2 were   8 was
3 were   9 were
4 wasn't   10 were
5 was   11 was
6 weren't

3
1 The 2004 Athens Olympics weren't a success.
2 I wasn't at home yesterday.
3 We weren't on holiday last week.
4 He wasn't ill on Monday.
5 The city wasn't very modern.
6 The athletes weren't very happy.

4
1 was, wasn't
2 wasn't, was
3 weren't, were
4 wasn't, was

5
1 was = 2   3 were = 1
2 was = 4   4 were = 3

LISTENING

1
1 T   2 F   3 T   4 F   5 F

2
1 c   2 b   3 d   4 a

GRAMMAR

1
1 called   3 needed
2 looked   4 believed

2
1 hated   5 called
2 travelled   6 asked
3 needed   7 worked
4 believed

3
1 b   2 a   3 a   4 b   5 a

PRONUNCIATION

1
1 /d/   2 /ɪd/   3 /t/   4 /ɪd/
5 /t/   6 /d/   7 /t/

LIVING IELTS

1 spectacular   3 dramatic
2 amazing   4 definitely

WRITING

1
1 Portugal   3 2004
2 500 000   4 1998

2
1 capital city
2 medium-sized
3 population
4 historical
5 centre
6 lively

3

Suggested answers
1 capital
2 medium-sized
3 centre

4

Cologne is a modern and lively city. The city is on the River Rhine, in the west of Germany. It is a large city with a population of more than one million. The main industries are insurance and media.In 2006, Cologne was one of the German cities to host the World Cup.

STUDY SKILLS

1
1 e   2 a   3 b   4 c   5 d

UNIT 6
VOCABULARY

1
1 a volunteer
2 full time
3 a job
4 experience
5 well-paid
6 new skills

2
1 job
2 volunteer
3 new skills
4 full time
5 well-paid
6 experience

LISTENING

1
3

2
1 a talk
2 Yes, she did.
3 doughnuts
4 another student

3
1 F   2 T   3 F   4 F

GRAMMAR

1
1 b   2 a   3 a   4 a   5 b

2
2 Yes, she did. She didn't take it.
3 No, they didn't. They got a job.
4 Yes, he did. He didn't get an interview.
5 No, they didn't. They came to visit him.

3
1 When   4 Where
2 How   5 Why
3 What

4
2 How long did he work there?
3 Did he like his job?
4 Why did he like it?
5 Where did he work?
6 Why did he leave?

READING

1 c

2
1 B   2 C   3 A   4 D

3
1 F   2 F   3 F   4 T   5 F   6 T

4
1 e   2 c   3 a   4 b   5 d

5
a increase
b government
c popular
d degree
e benefit

GRAMMAR

1
1 did   7 learned/learnt
2 felt   8 made
3 found   9 met
4 got   10 spent
5 gave   11 wrote
6 had

2
2 I didn't meet my parents at the weekend.
3 I didn't buy a new suit for the job.
4 I didn't learn a lot of interesting things.
5 I didn't get the job.
6 I didn't find the office easily.
7 I didn't have lunch with my manager.
8 I didn't write a lot of emails.
9 I didn't give a 20-minute presentation.
10 I didn't feel tired at the end of the day.

LIVING IELTS

1 happy   3 nervous
2 confident

PRONUNCIATION

1 /ə/   2 /e/   3 /iː/   4 /iː/
5 /e/   6 /ə/

WRITING

1
1 c   2 a   3 e   4 b   5 d

2
1 earn money
2 get work experience
3 develop language skills

3
1 I could earn money
2 I could get experience
3 they could develop language skills

4
My brother studies Business at a University in London. It is very expensive to live in London, [1] **so** he works as a waiter in an Italian restaurant at the weekends. He eats for free at the restaurant, [2] **so** he doesn't need to buy a lot of food. After his degree he wants to work for an international bank, [3] **so** he is also studying Spanish and German. My parents want him to get some work experience in a bank, [4] **so** they are not happy about his job in the restaurant. He knows my parents are right about this, [5] **so** he is now looking for a job in a bank.

STUDY SKILLS

1
1   4   5

UNIT 7
READING

1
1 a   2 c   3 c   4 a

2
1 combine
2 touch
3 Opposite
4 popular
5 sponsor

GRAMMAR

1
1 have to
2 don't have to, can
3 can't
4 can
5 can, have to
6 can
7 has to, has to
8 have to

2
1 can't   4 can't
2 can't   5 can
3 can   6 can

Answer Key

3
2 have to, have to
3 don't have to, have to
4 don't have to, have to

PRONUNCIATION
1 strong   3 strong
2 weak   4 weak

VOCABULARY
1
1 bounce   4 jump
2 Balance   5 hit
3 kick   6 climb

2
A basketball   D long jump
B gymnastics   E tennis
C rugby   F climbing

3
1 volleyball   5 climbing
2 tennis   6 golf
3 karate   7 basketball
4 gymnastics

GRAMMAR
1
1 picture C   4 picture F
2 picture A   5 picture B
3 picture E   6 picture D

2
1 c 2 a 3 e 4 f 5 b 6 d

3
1 need   4 don't need
2 don't need   5 don't need
3 need   6 need

4
e b c a f d

5
1 You don't need **to** be tall to do the long jump.
2 Do you **need~~s~~** to be very fit to play ping pong?
3 You **need~~ing~~** 11 people to make a football team.
4 You **do** not need a racket to do judo.
5 ~~Need you~~ **Do you need** a new tennis racket?

LISTENING
1
1 b 2 a 3 b 4 b 5 a 6 b

2
1 Y 2 N 3 N 4 N

3
1 a 2 c 3 b 4 a 5 c 6 c
7 a 8 b

LIVING IELTS
1 such   4 so
2 absolutely   5 really
3 even

WRITING
1
1 why people don't do sport
2 don't have time, find it boring, aren't good at it, have a medical condition
3 don't have time
4 have a medical condition

2
1 shows   4 Twenty-five
2 key   5 one in five
3 Fifty per cent 6 smallest

3
1 because they are getting too old
2 because they have an injury
3 because they don't have time
4 because they don't enjoy it anymore

4
Sample answer
The pie chart shows the different reasons people stop doing sport. Firstly, forty-five per cent of people stop doing sport because they are getting too old. Secondly, twenty-five per cent stop doing sport because they have an injury. Twenty per cent stop doing sport because they don't have time. Finally, ten per cent stop doing sports because they don't enjoy it anymore.

STUDY SKILLS
2
Andre – 1 and 3
Carole – 2 and 4

3
subjects: Biology, Sociology, Law, Engineering
verbs for sports: climb, hit, jump, kick
places to live: flat, house, bedsit, student hall
adjectives: awful, amazing, interesting, boring

EXAM SKILLS
1
1 an important historical building
2 three main points (and one final point)
3 say why you like the building

2
1 why it is important
2 where it is
3 what it looks like
4 why you like the building

3

	Chen Chen	Juan
doesn't give a long answer		✓
doesn't include all the points	✓	✓
doesn't follow the order of the points		✓

EXAM TIP
1 prepare   3 organise
2 notes

UNIT 8
VOCABULARY
1
1 rainforest, river   5 ocean
2 coast   6 waves
3 beach   7 waterfall
4 cliffs

2
1 unique   4 spectacular
2 scenery   5 destination
3 landscape

LISTENING
1
1 Y 2 Y 3 N 4 N 5 N 6 N

2
1 last year
2 when she was a child
3 4 years ago
4 last winter (for the first time)

VOCABULARY
1
1 beach   4 mountains
2 river   5 rainforest
3 view   6 volcano

2
1 sandy beaches
2 snowy mountains
3 spectacular views
4 extinct volcanoes
5 deep river
6 thick forests

LIVING IELTS
1
1 Wow   3 Surfing
2 great   4 exciting

2

1 Wow
2 exciting
3 Scuba diving
4 great

GRAMMAR

1

1 've never gone
2 've travelled
3 haven't finished
4 don't fly / never fly
5 visited

2

1 ~~Did you ever go~~ Have you ever been to Vietnam?
3 ~~Have~~ Has she ever been surfing?
6 ~~Did she ever eat~~ Has she ever eaten sushi?

3

1 Have, met
2 Did, meet
3 Have, been
4 Were
5 Did, play
6 Have, played

READING

1

1 C   2 B   3 D   4 A

2

1 F   2 F   3 T   4 T   5 T   6 T

GRAMMAR

1

1 c   2 a   3 b

2

1 for
2 How long
3 since
4 How long
5 since
6 for

3

1 We've been in Japan **for** a month.
3 She's loved surfing **for** many years.
5 They've worked here **since** 2010.

PRONUNCIATION

1

1 Have you been to Madagascar?
2 Yes, I <u>have</u>.
3 Has he seen a lemur?
4 No, he <u>hasn't</u>.

WRITING

1

a A gap year is a year off from studying. It happens after school and before university. Students often use the year to go travelling abroad.

b time to decide what they want to study and what job they want in the future, learn more about the world

c a long holiday and students forget how to study

2

1 D   2 A   3 B   4 C

3

1 However
2 In my opinion
3 First of all
4 For example

4

1 First of all
2 For example
3 However
4 In my opinion

5

Sample answer

Many students want to take a gap year. First of all, it gives students the chance to experience different things. For example, students can get valuable experience of work or travel to another country and learn about another culture. They can learn another language too. However, many people argue it is a long holiday and it isn't important in developing skills for future life. In my opinion, a gap year is an important experience for a student.

STUDY SKILLS

1

1 b   2 e   3 c   4 f   5 d   6 a

2

a There are many international students in the UK.

b I went to the shopping mall yesterday.

c He works for a large IT company.

d It is difficult to communicate in another language.

e You need to refer to the chart.

f Many children fail in school because they are tested too much.

3

Many students in the UK take a gap year after school. They want to see other countries before going to university. They can see the world and experience a new culture. For many it is the best year of their life. It doesn't have to be a long holiday – many people work. There is the argument that people should work to pay for university.

4

organised
grammar
spelling

EXAM SKILLS

1

1 50
2 116
3 2:40
4 7th
5 £53
6 777289
7 58
8 07889 471147

2

Numbers: 3
What? Event
Where? Place

3

1 Reception
2 meet the teachers and director
3 10.30
4 English test

4

five

5

1 T   2 F   3 F   4 T

6

1 Main Hall (MH)
2 Toilet (T)
3 Staff Room (SR)
4 Classroom (CR)
5 Library (L)

EXAM TIP

1 predict
2 Revise
3 Read

UNIT 9

VOCABULARY

1 big
2 come from
3 an only child
4 the youngest child
5 the middle child
6 the oldest child

READING

1

1 F   2 T   3 F   4 T   5 F

2

1 B   2 A   3 E   4 C   5 D

3

1 T   2 F   3 F   4 T   5 T
6 F   7 F   8 T   9 T

4

1 B   2 A   3 C

GRAMMAR

1

1 celebrate
2 give
3 make
4 save
5 spend
6 speak

2
1 are given
2 are spoken
3 is celebrated
3 are made
4 is spent
5 is saved

3
1 b   2 c   3 a   4 d

4
1 are celebrated
2 are invited
3 is called
4 is known
5 are celebrated
6 are given

VOCABULARY

1
Claudia = grandmother
Alfredo = grandfather
Lucia = mother
Roberto = father
Claudio = brother-in-law
Donatella = sister-in-law

2
1 cousin
2 aunts, uncles
3 son
4 daughter
5 niece
6 nephew

GRAMMAR

1
1 They eat different food in Kodinhi.
2 They drink different drinks in Kodinhi.
3 Doctors don't believe it is genetic.
4 Scientists need to do more research.

2
1 have
2 are located
3 are spread
4 is eaten
5 eat
6 is taken
7 use
8 live

LISTENING

1
a = 2   d = 5
b = 4   e = 3
c = 1

2
1 F   2 F   3 F   4 T   5 F   6 F

3
1 Where is it located?
2 Why is it special?
3 How many twins are normally born in Asia?
4 Who normally has twins?

LIVING IELTS

1 far   4 do
2 do   5 like most
3 really   6 do

WRITING

1
a The cost of raising a child in the UK
b 2003, 2006, and 2009
c increasing
d childcare, education and food

2
1 total
2 childcare
3 thousand
4 food
5 clothing

3
1 Personal expenses cost the least.
2 Holidays cost more than babysitting.
3 Childcare costs the most.
4 Hobbies and toys cost almost the same as babysitting.
5 Clothing is twice the cost of leisure and recreation.

4
Sample answer
The cost of raising a child was nearly £60 000 more in 2009 than 2003. Childcare costs the most at nearly £55 000. Holidays cost more than babysitting, but this is almost the same as hobbies and toys. Clothing is nearly twice the cost of leisure and recreation. Personal expenses are the least expensive thing at just over £1 000.

STUDY SKILLS

2
1 most common use
2 sound file
3 phonetic script
4 part of speech
5 definition
6 example sentence

EXAM SKILLS

1
1 c   2 a   3 b   4 d

2
3   4   2   1

3
1 first sentence
2 order
3 details
4 not given

4
1 N   2 NG   3 Y

EXAM TIP

1 multiple   3 spend
2 text   4 understand

UNIT 10
READING

1
1 people using the world's resources
2 gallons of water used by an American family in one day
3 The Aral lake started getting smaller.
4 The lake lost nearly 95% of its size.

2
1 b   2 a   3 d   4 c

3
1 F   2 F   3 F   4 T   5 T   6 T

4
1 a   2 b   3 a   4 b

GRAMMAR

1

Countable nouns	Uncountable nouns
city	advice
professor	coffee
job	food
flat	money
test	music
friend	traffic
concert	information

2
1 U   2 U   3 C   4 C   5 U   6 C

3
1 any   4 a
2 any   5 some
3 some

4
1 People are causing ~~a~~ damage to many rivers.
2 The weather isn't causing ~~some~~ any of the changes.
3 ~~Any~~ Many/Some people lost their jobs.
4 It was ~~some~~ **a** good ~~suggestions~~ suggestion.

Listening

1
A bald eagle   C grey wolf
B giant panda   D humpback whale

2
1 b   2 a   3 d   4 c

3
1 417   3 2000
2 1.3 billion   4 1930s

4
1 T   2 T   3 F   4 T

Grammar

1
1 How much?   4 How much?
2 How much?   5 How many?
3 How many?

2
1 How many   3 How many
2 How much   4 How much

3
1 b   2 c   3 b   4 b

4
2 ~~much~~ many
4 ~~many~~ much
5 ~~much~~ many

Vocabulary

1
noun: conservation, destruction, extinction, pollution
verb: conserve, destroy, pollute

2
1 destruction
2 pollute
3 conserve
4 extinction

Pronunciation

1
oO
destroy, pollute, conserve, extinct
oOo
destruction
extinction
pollution
ooOo
conservation

Living IELTS

1 B   2 A   3 C

Writing

1
Man is destroying Earth. Describe three ways we can stop this.

2
a   c   e

3
a 2   b 4   c 3   d 1

4
a 3   b 1   c 4   d 2

5
Sample answer
The seas are becoming polluted around the world. This is happening because people are throwing too much rubbish into the sea. To solve this problem we need to take three steps. Firstly, we need to produce less rubbish. Secondly, we need to find ways to deal with rubbish. Finally, we need solutions to clean our seas. In this way, we can help the seas around the world.

Study Skills

2
a 2, 4   c 1, 3
b 4   d 5

3
1 be organised and set priorities
2 sleep for eight hours
3 take breaks
4 exercise
5 try to relax
6 eat healthy food
7 reward yourself

Exam Skills

1
1   2   4   and   5

2
intro: 1 what the different sources of energy are.
agree: 2 examples of how we can change our behaviour.
disagree: 4 the cost of different energy sources.
conclusion: 5 why it's important to change our behaviour.

3
1 however, also, although
2 also
3 however, although

Exam Tip

1 carefully
2 brainstorm
3 organise
4 link

UNIT 11

Vocabulary

1
Across
6 heavy
7 expensive
9 fast

Down
1 boring
2 cheap
3 safe
4 efficient
5 modern
8 dangerous

2
1 boring   5 inefficient
2 expensive   6 old-fashioned
3 safe   7 slow
4 heavy

Reading

2
A The International Space Station
B The Alraj Al Bait Towers
C The Jiaozhou Bay Bridge
D The Bailong elevator

3
1 F   2 F   3 T   4 F
5 T   6 T   7 F

4
1 more expensive   3 smaller
2 higher   4 longer

Grammar

1

add -r	safer
add -er	smaller lighter faster longer
double the final consonant and add -er	bigger hotter
take off the -y and add -ier	happier heavier
add *more*	more expensive more comfortable more beautiful more boring
irregular	good = better bad = worse

2
1 happier   5 more comfortable
2 longer   6 heavier
3 smaller   7 hotter
4 more expensive   8 bigger

Answer Key

3
Sample answers

The Hummer H2 is more inefficient than the Kia Rio.

The Kia Rio is lighter than the Hummer H2.

The Hummer H2 is heavier than the Kia Rio.

The Kia Rio is faster than the Hummer H2.

The Hummer H2 is slower than the Kia Rio.

PRONUNCIATION

1
It's bigg**er** t**h**an this one.
It's heavi**er** t**h**an the others.
It's much strong**er** t**h**an before.
It old**er** t**h**an the others.

GRAMMAR

1
2 the most beautiful
3 the heaviest
4 the tallest
5 the most expensive
6 the largest
7 the longest
8 the strongest
9 the ugliest
10 the worst

2
1 the ugliest
2 the tallest
3 the most expensive
4 the worst
5 the strongest
6 the most beautiful

3
1 That is the **longest** bridge in Mexico.
2 Mount Everest is **the** highest mountain in the world.
3 The London Underground is the **oldest** in the world.
4 The Sahara is the **biggest** desert in the world.
5 Russia is **the** biggest country in the world.
6 Kilimanjaro is the **highest** mountain in Africa.
7 The Shard is the **tallest** building in London.
8 Luanda is the **most** expensive city in the world.

LISTENING

1
1 E   1950s remote control
2 A   1960s computer mouse
3 D   1970s mobile phone
4 C   1980s Microsoft
5 F   1990s internet
6 B   2000s iPhone

3
1 b   2 b   3 b   4 a   5 b   6 b

LIVING IELTS

1
1 a lot   3 so much
2 really   4 really

2
1 c   2 a   3 d   4 b

WRITING

1
cost
time to build
distance from the city centre
people in the building

2
Building 1

3
1 paragraph 3
2 paragraph 1
3 paragraph 2

4
Building 1 can house the largest number of people. However, it is the most expensive choice and it also takes the longest time to build. Building 2 and Building 3 cost the same. However, Building 3 is smaller, takes longer to build and houses fewer people.
I think Building 1 is the best choice. It is slower to build than the others and more expensive, but it is the closest to the city centre and can hold more people.

EXAM SKILLS

Speaking
2
Candidate A: improve on points 1, 3, 4, 6
Candidate B: good at 1, 4, 6, 7

Listening
2
1   2   5   6

3
1 Greenfield   4 June
2 P54 2QR   5 21
3 07889 64758

UNIT 12

LISTENING

1
Raouf C
Sergy A
Ana B

2
1 T   2 T   3 T   4 F   5 F   6 NG

3
1 Raouf   4 Raouf
2 Sergy   5 Ana
3 Sergy

VOCABULARY

1
Take a coffee. ✗ We say *to have or to make* a coffee. ✓

Do a mistake. ✗ We say *to make a mistake.* ✓

Make business ✗ We say *to do business* (with someone). ✓

Have a decision ✗ We say *to make a decision* (about something or someone). ✓

2
1 do an internship
2 make money
3 have lunch
4 make a presentation
5 take an exam
6 do a degree
7 have a problem
8 take a photo

3
1 into   5 for
2 with   6 in
3 on
4 at

4
1 do an internship
2 have fun
3 make/earn money
4 have plans
5 make plans

5
1 at
2 for
3 at
4 about
5 around

6
1 getting off
2 We're off
3 far off

GRAMMAR

1
1 are, going to
2 is, going to
3 isn't, going to
4 are, going to
5 aren't, going to

2
a 2   b 4   c 1   d 3   e 5

3
1 Maria ~~is~~ **is** going to go by car to the coast.
3 My parents ~~is~~ are going to work this weekend.
5 It ~~are~~ is going to be a difficult week.

4

Miguel: Alex, are you going to do anything this weekend?   1

Alex: No, no plans? Why? Do you have any ideas?   2

Miguel: Well, yes. I'm going to see Adele in concert.   3

Alex: Adele! I'd love to see her! She's a great singer.   4

Miguel: I have an extra ticket. Do you want to go?   5

Alex: Sure! When is it?   6

Miguel: On Sunday evening.   7

Alex: Oh, no, I can't! I'm going to have dinner with my classmates.   8

PRONUNCIATION

1
1 gəʊɪŋtə
2 gəʊɪŋtə
3 gəʊɪŋ
4 gəʊɪŋ
5 gəʊɪŋtə
6 gəʊɪŋ

READING

1 3

2
1 C   2 B   3 C   4 A   5 D   6 B

3
1 a   2 e   3 d   4 b   5 c

GRAMMAR

1
B Students learning Arabic <u>will</u> have a teacher based in the Middle East. They <u>won't</u> be in the classroom together – they <u>will</u> connect on the internet. Schools <u>won't</u> have to go on expensive trips to other countries. They <u>will</u> take virtual tours of some of the most famous Arabian sites. Then they <u>will</u> have a conversation with Arabic students in Arabic.

C Students <u>won't</u> take tests with a pen and paper. All tests <u>will</u> be done on a computer. They <u>won't</u> be marked by a teacher. The computer <u>will</u> mark the test. Parents <u>will</u> be able to download electronic copies of everything their child does.

D In Korea the government has said all Korean text books <u>will</u> be available electronically by 2015. Some parts of the world <u>won't</u> take long to catch up. So how long until we <u>will</u> never read a paper book again?

2
1 won't replace
2 will use
3 won't read
4 won't travel, will visit
5 won't be, will buy
6 won't be, will be

LIVING IELTS

1 hard   2 think

WRITING

2

	David	Jane
1	✓	✗
2	✓	✗
3	✓	✗
4	✓	✓

3
David

4
She disagrees because she thinks the relationship between the student and the teacher is really important and this will not change.

5
1 opinion
2 think
3 don't agree
4 don't believe
5 disagree

7
1 In my opinion, public libraries will disappear in the future.
2 I don't think checkout assistants in supermarkets will be replaced by machines.
3 I think bicycles will replace cars in the future.
4 I don't agree that most people will smoke cigarettes in the future.
5 I think most people won't eat meat in the future.
6 I don't believe all cars will be electric in the future.

9
Sample answer
In my opinion, teachers in the future will not be replaced by computers. I think teachers give important help to students and computers cannot always help students.
We will use computers more in education, but I don't agree that teachers will be replaced by computers. I think students need to talk to teachers and ask questions. Teachers can answer the questions and check students understand. They can support students. Students also need teachers to make learning interesting. A computer cannot encourage students. For this reason, I do not believe teachers will be replaced by computers.

EXAM SKILLS

Writing
2
Do the <u>advantages</u> of <u>studying abroad</u> <u>outweigh</u> the <u>disadvantages</u>? What <u>advice</u> would you offer to <u>someone planning</u> to <u>study abroad</u>?

3
advantages: new culture, learn a language, good for future job, good universities

disadvantages: miss home, problems communicating, expensive, harder work

4
What advice would you offer to someone planning to study abroad?

5
b   c   a   or   c   b   a

Reading
3
1 People will not take <u>holidays</u> in <u>other countries</u> so much.
2 People do <u>not</u> take <u>holidays</u> in their <u>own country today</u>.
3 <u>Gap years</u> will still be <u>popular</u>.
4 People will <u>travel less</u> for <u>everything</u>.

4
1 Y   2 NG   3 N   4 Y   facts

Irregular verbs

INFINITIVE	PAST SIMPLE	PAST PARTICIPLE
be	was/were	been
become	became	become
begin	began /bɪˈgæn/	begun /bɪˈgʌn/
bet	bet	bet
bite /baɪt/	bit	bitten /ˈbɪtən/
blow /bləʊ/	blew /bluː/	blown /bləʊn/
break	broke	broken
bring	brought /brɔːt/	brought
build /bɪld/	built /bɪlt/	built
burn	burnt	burnt
buy	bought /bɔːt/	bought
catch	caught /kɔːt/	caught
choose	chose /tʃəʊz/	chosen
come	came	come
cost	cost	cost
cut	cut	cut
do	did	done
draw /drɔː/	drew /druː/	drawn /drɔːn/
dream	dreamt	dreamt
drink	drank /dræŋk/	drunk /drʌŋk/
drive	drove	driven
eat	ate /eɪt/	eaten /ˈiːtən/
fall /fɔːl/	fell /fel/	fallen /ˈfɔːlən/
feel /fiːl/	felt /felt/	felt
fight /faɪt/	fought /fɔːt/	fought
find	found /faʊnd/	found
flee	flew	flown
fly /flaɪ/	flew /fluː/	flown /fləʊn/
forget	forgot	forgotten
forgive	forgave	forgiven
freeze	froze	frozen
get	got	got
give	gave	given
go	went	been/gone
grow /grəʊ/	grew /gruː/	grown /grəʊn/
hang /hæŋ/	hung /hʌŋ/	hung
have	had	had
hear /hɪə/	heard /hɜːd/	heard /hɜːd/
hide	hid	hidden /ˈhɪdən/
hit	hit	hit
hold	held	held
hurt /hɜːt/	hurt	hurt
keep	kept	kept
know /nəʊ/	knew /njuː/	known /nəʊn/
lay /leɪ/	laid	laid
lead /liːd/	led /led/	led
learn /lɜːn/	learnt	learnt
leave	left	left
lend	lent	lent

INFINITIVE	PAST SIMPLE	PAST PARTICIPLE
let	let	let
lie (in bed)	lay	lain
lie (not tell the truth)	lied	lied
lose /luːz/	lost	lost
make	made	made
mean	meant	meant
meet	met	met
pay /peɪ/	paid /peɪd/	paid
prove	proved	proven/proved
put	put	put
read /riːd/	read /red/	read /red/
ride	rode	ridden
ring	rang /ræŋ/	rung /rʌŋ/
run /rʌn/	ran /ræn/	run
say /seɪ/	said /sed/	said
see	saw /sɔː/	seen
sell	sold	sold
send	sent	sent
set	set	set
shoot	shot	shot
show	showed	shown
shut	shut	shut
sing	sang /sæŋ/	sung /sʌŋ/
sink	sank /sæŋk/	sunk /sʌŋk/
sit	sat	sat
sleep	slept	slept
slide	slid	slid
speak	spoke	spoken
spell	spelt	spelt
spend	spent	spent
spoil	spoilt	spoilt
spread /spred/	spread	spread
stand	stood	stood
steal	stole	stolen
stick	stuck /stʌk/	stuck
strike /straɪk/	struck /strʌk/	struck
swear	swore	sworn
swim	swam /swæm/	swum /swʌm/
take /teɪk/	took /tʊk/	taken /ˈteɪkən/
teach	taught /tɔːt/	taught
tell	told	told
think	thought /θɔːt/	thought
throw /θrəʊ/	threw /θruː/	thrown /θrəʊn/
understand	understood	understood
wake	woke /wəʊk/	woken /ˈwəʊkən/
wear /weə/	wore /wɔː/	worn /wɔːn/
win	won /wʌn/	won
write	wrote	written /ˈrɪtən/